FOUNDATIONS

in PERSONAL FINANCE®

High School Edition

DAVE RAMSEY

Acknowledgements

The Ramsey Education Solutions team would like to give special thanks to the following people for their contributions to this product. Their input was essential for creating a financial literacy curriculum that empowers high school students to make sound financial decisions for life.

Educators

Len McKnatt
ACCOUNTING/ECONOMICS TEACHER
Battle Ground Academy
Franklin, Tennessee

Leah Zimmer
FINANCIAL LITERACY TEACHER
Bremerton High School
Bremerton, Washington

Brittany Sampson
TEACHER
Lakeland High School
Lakeland, Florida

Ramona Harper
BUSINESS TEACHER
Lake Highlands High School
Richardson, Texas

Kathy Jarman
TEACHER
Helias Catholic High School
Jefferson City, Missouri

LeAnn Dinsdale
CTE TEACHER/ACTE VP
Brackenridge High School
San Antonio, Texas

Lynn Isaacks
SOCIAL STUDIES TEACHER
Academy of Creative Education
San Antonio, Texas

Eric Lambert
TEACHER
North Bullitt High School
Shepherdsville, Kentucky

Linda Brown
CTE TEACHER
Sanderson High School
Raleigh, North Carolina

Terri Winkle
TEACHER
Western Heights High School
Oklahoma City, Oklahoma

Credits

Executive Vice President
Jack Galloway

Chief Marketing Officer
Jennifer Sievertsen

Senior Vice President of Education Solutions
Jim King

Curriculum Design
Michelle Scott

Product Management
Brett Kozimor

Sales/Marketing/PR
Herb Jenkins
Beth Tallent
Jacqueline Garneau
Jamie Moorer
Christy Richardson
Christy Wright

Project Management
Josh Campbell
Kassidy Slamer
Lisa Mays

Content Editing/Proofing
Allen Harris
Darcie Clemen
Stephanie Thomas
Brandon Brison
Jennifer Gingerich
Danielle Britt
Jennifer Norton
Molly Pinkley

Creative Design
Brian Williams
Marcus Meazzo
Jason Miller
Steve Rupp

Video/Audio Production
Jon Melton
Diana Key
Megan Hill
Josh Fulton
Dave Oglesby
Dave DiCicco
Megan Ledford
Sara Zellner
Chris Wright
Ian Collins
Colin Fatke
Bobby Robertson
David Wilkinson
Josh Hancock
Chris Blaylock

Interactive/Web Development/UI
Ash Harris
Jon Wolski
Andrew Kallemeyn

Meet the Experts

Dave Ramsey

America's trusted voice on money and business, Dave Ramsey is a personal money-management expert and extremely popular national radio personality. His company, Ramsey Solutions, offers a message of hope, through various means, to anyone who wants to better understand the principles of proper money management. Dave has authored eight best-selling books, including three #1 national best sellers. *The Dave Ramsey Show* is heard by more than 12 million listeners each week on more than 575 radio stations and digitally through podcasts, online audio streaming, and a 24-hour online streaming video channel.

Rachel Cruze

As a seasoned communicator and Ramsey Personality, Rachel Cruze has been speaking to groups as large as 10,000 for more than a decade. The daughter of Dave Ramsey, she joined Ramsey Solutions in 2010 and uses the knowledge and experiences from growing up in the Ramsey household to educate others on the proper way to handle their money wisely and stay out of debt. Rachel co-authored the #1 *New York Times* best-selling book *Smart Money Smart Kids* with her dad. Her new book, *Love Your Life, Not Theirs*, released October 2016. You can follow Rachel on Twitter and Instagram at @RachelCruze and online at rachelcruze.com, youtube.com/rachelcruze or facebook.com/rachelramseycruze.

Chris Hogan

A popular and dynamic speaker on the topics of personal finance, retirement and leadership, Chris Hogan helps people across the country develop successful strategies to manage their money in both their personal lives and businesses. He is the host of the Retire Inspired Podcast and the author of *Retire Inspired: It's Not an Age; It's a Financial Number*, a #1 national best seller. For more than a decade, Chris has served at Ramsey Solutions as a trusted financial coach and Ramsey Personality. You can follow Chris on Twitter and Instagram at @ChrisHogan360 and online at chrishogan360.com or facebook.com/chrishogan360.

Contents

CHAPTER 1

What do other high school students know about spending?

We asked other high school students if they or someone they know has ever bought something they could not afford.

....

"I haven't, but my younger sister always seems to need the latest and greatest technology, and she spends her college money on it!"

Sophomore, Louisiana

"No. But I have a family member who once bought a house that they ended up not being able to afford."

Junior, New Jersey

"My dad bought a car that he could not afford, and he ended up getting it repossessed."

Junior, Wyoming

"Yes. My parents buy things they can't afford all the time. That's why we're in debt. That's why I need this course."

Senior, Utah

Introduction to Personal Finance

81%

of parents feel it is their responsibility to teach their kids about money and savings.*

85%

of American parents surveyed thought that a course in personal finance should be a high school graduation requirement.*

WELCOME TO A CLASS that is going to give you a head start on your future! Learning how to manage your money is one of the most important skills you can have. Why? Because your financial decisions will have long-term consequences, either good or bad. We'll give you the tools and knowledge that will help you win with money right from the start. When it comes to your financial future, we want you to aim high and dream big. There's a lot to learn, so let's get started!

*National Foundation for Credit Counseling, Inc.

Before You Begin

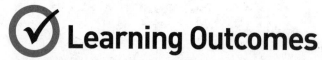 Learning Outcomes

Once you've completed this chapter's videos, you will be asked to return to this list and place a checkmark next to the items you've mastered.

Section 1: What Is Personal Finance?

☐ Describe what personal finance is.

☐ Outline the components of effective financial planning.

☐ Identify focuses of study throughout this course.

Section 2: Money, the American Way

☐ Understand the evolution of America's dependence on credit.

☐ Observe and analyze the "normal" American family as it relates to personal finance.

Section 3: You and Money

☐ Develop communication strategies for managing money and discussing financial issues.

☐ Evaluate your own money personality; identify your money strengths and weaknesses.

 Key Terms

Get to know the language of money.

» **Consumer:** A person or organization that uses a product or service

» **Credit:** The granting of a loan and the creation of debt; any form of deferred payment

» **Debt:** An obligation of repayment owed by one party (the debtor/borrower) to a second party (the creditor/lender); in most cases this includes repayment of the original loan amount plus interest

» **Economy:** A system by which goods and services are produced and distributed

» **Financial literacy:** The knowledge and skillset necessary to be an informed consumer and manage finances effectively

» **Interest:** A fee paid by a borrower to the lender for the use of borrowed money; typically interest is calculated as a percentage of the principal (original loan amount)

» **Loan:** A debt evidenced by a "note," which specifies the principal amount, interest rate and date of repayment

» **Personal finance:** All of the decisions and activities of an individual or family regarding their money, including spending, saving, budgeting, etc.

Measure Your Progress

Before watching the video, read each statement below and mark whether you agree or disagree in the "Before" column. Then, after watching the video, do it again using the "After" column to see if you changed your mind on any statement.

BEFORE			AFTER	
Agree	Disagree		Agree	Disagree
☐	☐	1. I already have a strong working knowledge of personal finance.	☐	☐
☐	☐	2. I think I have a lot to learn when it comes to managing money.	☐	☐
☐	☐	3. Because I am a teenager, what I do now with my money will have little effect on my financial future.	☐	☐
☐	☐	4. My parents have taught me a lot about how to manage money.	☐	☐
☐	☐	5. Most Americans are very wealthy and will have financial security when they retire.	☐	☐

JOURNAL QUESTION: INTRODUCTION

Can you think of a financial goal you have at this moment? Is this a long-term or a short-term goal? Describe how you plan to achieve this financial goal.

_____

_____

_____

This is one of the most important classes you will ever take. We're excited you are joining us. Now let's begin!

"Wealth is more often the result of a lifestyle of hard work, perseverance, planning and, most of all, self-discipline."

The Millionaire Next Door

55% of teens surveyed say that they want to learn more about how to manage their money— particularly learning about: **investing** (88%), **saving** (87%), **budgeting** (82%), **checking accounts** (80%), and financing for **big purchase**s like a car or a home (79%).

National Foundation for Credit Counseling, Inc.

CHAPTER 1

Section 1:
What Is Personal Finance?

MOST HIGH SCHOOL students don't spend their time worrying about mortgages and investments, but they are at an age when smaller financial responsibilities start creeping into their lives. Many of you are earning allowances or have already begun working a part-time job. So what do you do with your money? If you're just putting it in your pocket and spending without a plan, living payday to payday could become your normal. You need to make decisions about what to do with your money.

Have a money plan. Set money goals. Learning to manage money at this stage can eliminate financial mistakes and promote huge financial benefits for the future.

What is personal finance? Personal finance refers to all the financial decisions an individual or family must make in order to earn, budget, save and spend money over time. These decisions are generally based on a variety of financial risks and planning for the future.

Key Components of Financial Planning

Directions: *As you see words pop up on the left side of the video screen, write them into the workbook blanks.*

Assess your _____ situation (your income, assets and liabilities).
₁

Set money _____! Make sure you have a mix of both short-term and long-term goals.
₂

You must write out a detailed _____ for accomplishing your goals. This begins with your budget.
₃

_____ your plan! This involves discipline and perseverance.
₄

Know your money _____.
₅

Regularly _____ and reassess your financial plan.
₆

Replace money _____ with money truths.
₇

JOURNAL QUESTION: VIDEO 1.1

In what ways could you do better when it comes to managing your money?

_____

_____

_____

Two in **five** U.S. adults gave themselves a C, D or F on their knowledge of personal finance.

National Foundation for Credit Counseling, Inc.

"Wealth building isn't rocket science, which is a good thing for me (and probably you). Winning at money is 80% behavior and 20% head knowledge. What to do isn't the problem; doing it is. Most of us know what to do, but we just don't do it. If I can control the guy in the mirror, I can be rich. Find a mirror!"

DAVE RAMSEY

If you put into practice what we teach, you truly can win with money!

Section 2: Money, the American Way

VIDEO 2.1

A History of Credit and Consumerism

It is impossible to discuss the history of personal finance in America without highlighting the evolution of the credit industry. Think, for a moment, about the most recent commercial you've seen advertising a big ticket item like a new car or new furniture. Do those ads target people who have "budgeted,

PRIOR TO  1917 1929 1939

 1

Credit Prior to 1917

» Before 1917, buying things on credit was not common. Why? Because it had never been legal for lenders to charge interest rates high enough to turn a profit.

» Lending money to others was not a money-making business. Only wealthy people could get personal loans. Without the possibility of profit, lending money to the middle and lower class was not worth the risk.

» Small-time loan sharks (people who offered loans at extremely high interest rates, which was an illegal activity at the time) existed for people in desperate financial positions, but they were shady operations on the fringes of society.

» The highly evolved, highly accepted consumer credit as we know it today did not exist.

 2

Credit Takes Root

» After 1920, consumer demand for big-ticket manufactured products was on the rise.

» Credit laws were relaxed in an attempt to create a mainstream, profitable alternative to loan sharks for the working class.

» Installment credit (type of credit that has a fixed number of payments, also known as revolving credit) and legalized personal loans became big business.

» This era made consumer credit legal and more socially accepted.

"In 1917, one popular historian described debt as 'semi-slavery'... (which) existed before the dawn of history, and it exists today."

Debtor Nation: The History
of America in Red Ink

 3

Leveraging Credit to Escape the Great Depression

» In an attempt to help Americans regain their financial footing, New Deal policy-makers came up with mortgage (home loans) and consumer lending policies that convinced commercial banks that consumer credit could be profitable despite bankers' long-held reluctance to lend to the working class.

The New Deal was the legislative and administrative program of President F. D. Roosevelt designed to promote economic recovery and social reform during the 1930s.

Source: *Debtor Nation: The History of America in Red Ink*

saved, and are ready to go make that large purchase"? Or are they more likely to suggest that you "Buy NOW, pay LATER"? Which phrase is more familiar? Sadly, borrowing money is so ingrained in our culture that we can't imagine life without it. So how did we get here? Let's take a look.

 1945

 **1970** TO THE PRESENT

4

WWII Fuels an Economic Recovery

» After the Great Depression, WWII proved to be the most important economic event of the 20th century. The war ended the Great Depression by reviving American industry through government spending and consumption. In short, the economy improved because the war created a ton of new jobs. These jobs provided considerable increase in personal income and led Americans to predict permanent improvements to their standard of living.

"Americans left government-mortgaged homes in installment-financed cars to shop on revolving credit at shopping centers."

Debtor Nation

5

Post World War II Consumerism

» Ah, the birth of the suburbs! The post-war middle class bought the American Dream with consumer credit. Americans "learned" to borrow in the midst of prosperity.

» They borrowed because they believed their incomes would continue to grow into the future . . . and they were right. Incomes rose steadily from 1945 to 1970.

» Financial institutions lent more money, and borrowers paid it back. Borrowing became a post-war normalcy.

"If you will happen to your money, then you will have some. If you just let all your money happen to you, you'll never win."

DAVE RAMSEY

6

The Decline Into Debt: 1970–Present

» After 1970, consumer debt skyrocketed not because people were borrowing more, but because they continued to borrow as their parents had done since WWII. The difference was they didn't have the postwar period's well-paying jobs.

» Banks were willing to lend even more because they were now making huge profits off consumer debt. The credit industry had become smarter than borrowers.

» As consumers borrowed to deal with unexpected job losses and medical expenses, as well as to live "the good life," banks were willing to continue lending.

» Due to the clever structuring of financial institutions, the credit world now resembles the pre-1920s loan sharks more than the 1950s banks.

» In short, an old credit system premised on rising wages and stable employment (low-risk borrower) was reformed to accommodate uncertain employment and income instability (high-risk borrower).

Today's American Reality

Unfortunately, many American families only have the appearance of being financially secure. If you drive through a middle-class neighborhood, you might look at the manicured lawns, nice houses and new vehicles in the driveways and think, *Wow, they're doing all right. I want to live like that when I'm an adult.*

The sad reality is that most of the people in those houses are struggling with debt in the form of mortgages, car loans, student loans and credit cards. Based on statistics, Americans are horrible at saving money and planning for retirement. They are so conditioned to think debt is normal, they can't envision paying cash for a car or even a dining room table! Americans often spend more money than they make. Most Americans don't have an emergency fund. Saving, budgeting, retirement planning and staying out of debt are all basic money principles, not complex economics.

So why aren't Americans better at managing money? They were never taught the right way. As you go through this course, we will focus on teaching you what to do with money and then show you how to do it. Money math is easy. It's controlling your money behavior that's the challenge. As you evaluate the "normal" American family, consider your own financial future.

The fact is, this doesn't have to be your future reality.

» You don't have to spend more _____ than you make just to look good in front of your friends. You can learn basic money principles and put them into practice.

» When you manage money well, you'll experience deeper _____.

» It's really simple! Personal finance is 80% _____ and 20% head knowledge.

» Money _____ is easy—it's controlling your behavior that's the real challenge.

» As you think about the "_____" American family, remember that normal is broke. You don't have to be normal!

📊 A Snapshot of the "Normal" American Family

Don't be fooled by outside images of new cars and expensive homes. Most Americans are struggling financially and drowning in debt.

DEBT PROFILE OF THE AVERAGE AMERICAN FAMILY*	
Average Credit Card Debt (of households with credit card debt)	**$15,799**
Average Mortgage Debt	**$149,667**
Average Student Loan Debt	**$32,559**
Average Car Loan Debt	**$13,125**

This does *not* have to be your future reality. If you manage money well from the start and make the decision not to use debt as a financial tool, you can avoid the stress of living paycheck to paycheck.

✱ NOTE: Average credit card debt of all American households is $7,000, source: Nerd Wallet

*Federal Reserve, U.S. Census Bureau, Internal Revenue Service, manilla.com

Dave's Story

With more than 20 years of experience counseling people on how to manage their money, Dave knows what it takes to get control of your cash.

More than 20 years ago, my wife, Sharon, and I went broke. We lost everything due to my stupidity in handling money, or not handling it, as the case may be. Hitting bottom and hitting it hard was the worst thing that ever happened to me and the best thing that ever happened to me.

We started with nothing, but by the time I was 26 years old, we held real estate worth more than $4 million. I was good at real estate, but I was better at borrowing money. Even though I had become a millionaire, I had built a house of cards. The short version of the story is that debt caused us, over the course of two and a half years of fighting it, to lose everything. We were sued, foreclosed on, and, finally, with a brand-new baby and a toddler, we were bankrupt. Scared doesn't begin to cover it. Crushed comes close, but we held on to each other and decided we needed a change.

Dave's Story *(Continued)*

After losing everything, I went on a quest to find out how money really works, how I could get control of it, and how I could have confidence in handling it. I read everything I could get my hands on. I interviewed older rich people, people who made money and kept it. That quest led me to a really, really uncomfortable place: my mirror. I came to realize that my money problems, worries and shortages largely began and ended with the person in my mirror. I also realized that if I could learn to manage the character I shaved with every morning, I would win with money.

The stuff we teach in this class represents everything I've learned about money since then, from savings and debt, to insurance and investing. And I'm excited that my daughter Rachel has joined me to get this information to you before you graduate high school. Trust me, knowing this stuff then would have saved me a whole lot of trouble!

What's Your Money Personality?

StageofLife.com conducted a writing contest to evaluate students' attitudes toward money and the role of money in their lives. The following was the contest writing prompt:

> "What is your relationship with money? How do you spend (or save) and why?"

More than 3,335 students from all 50 U.S. states contributed a 500-word essay response. From the essay submissions, several themes emerged:

1. **FRUSTRATION:** Many teens expressed negative emotions about money: anger, frustration, stress, distrust and even hatred.

2. **ROLE MODELS:** Teens are watching how their parents treat money. In several of the essays, the teens made a point to criticize how their parents handle money and vowed not to "be like them."

3. **PRAGMATIC:** There was a minority voice that did approach the topic with a more pragmatic point of view and in some rarer cases, even positivity. Students shared their personal saving tips, budgeting experience and more.

4. **MONEY ISN'T EVERYTHING:** A good percentage of the essays address a more universal truth: that money isn't everything. Yes, it's needed to survive, but it's not a requirement in making people happy.

Americans Are Being Outsmarted

Ultimately, what made our current indebtedness possible was that it became profitable. Yes, a debt system that keeps Americans from achieving wealth and makes us "slaves" to the lender exists because it became a profitable industry. Today, with Americans charging more than a trillion dollars each year on their credit cards, one can understand why the credit card companies are so profitable. There is nothing wrong with a business turning a profit; what's wrong is that these companies are outsmarting Americans. That should bother you!

Why do we allow ourselves to be outsmarted when it comes to our own money?

» We like _____—lots of stuff!
   13

» We are told that debt is _____. It has become
   14
   acceptable in our culture to use credit to buy things.

» We are taught that we can _____ _____.
   15
   This is simply not true!

» Our debt system keeps us from building _____
   16
   because we are constantly giving our money away to pay
   for things we bought years ago.

» In America, we are bombarded with marketing ads that
   push us to buy things. "You can buy it today with no money
   down and no interest for 90 days!" Sound familiar?

» We want you to be _____ of the financial
   17
   condition of our country—and we want you to
   _____ it!
   18

We will talk more about consumerism and debt in later chapters. Right now, our focus is to be aware of the financial "condition" of America and begin to question it.

> "You will either manage your money, or the lack of it will always manage you."
>
> DAVE RAMSEY

JOURNAL QUESTION: VIDEO 2.1

What was Dave's biggest lesson when it came to managing money and building wealth?

_____

_____

_____

Section 3: You and Money

VIDEO 3.1

Learn the Language of Money

No one is born financially smart! Learning the language of personal finance is the first step in becoming money smart. The language of money is spoken in the vocabulary of accounting: understanding what credits, debits, assets and liabilities are. You've got to learn enough to understand your personal financial statements and communicate effectively about your finances. How smart you are with your money will determine your financial well-being in life.

» Knowing the _____ of money allows you to tell your money what to do. [19]

» That means deciding where your money is going to go _____ you get your paycheck. [20]

» You'll be able to communicate effectively with _____, financial planners and insurance agents. [21]

» Focus on understanding the _____ as you move through this course. [22]

» You'll become the _____ on your money. Winning with money is not complicated, but it does involve some basic knowledge. [23]

Learning the language is the key to the game.

Learning the language of money is a little bit like learning the language of sports. You can't really follow—much less enjoy—a football game if you don't know what the ref is talking about when he uses words like "blitz," "option" or "stunt." But once those terms are explained to you and you grasp their meaning in the context of the game, you can easily get into it and shout for your team.

It's the same way with money. Being financially literate allows you to participate in the game. And if you really put what you learn into practice, you can even become a coach—and tell your money what to do! Of course, that doesn't mean talking to your Benjamins. It's about effectively communicating with bankers, financial planners and insurance agents—people who provide the money services you need in order to grow wealth. It's also about knowing how to budget and what to budget for.

Understanding the language of money will allow you to manage your own finances effectively. You don't want to be dependent on outside influences to control, shape or coerce your financial behavior. Instead, *you* will determine which level of financial well-being you will achieve. It's simple. If you're going to tell your money what to do, you need to first speak the language!

> "Ignorance is not lack of intelligence; it is lack of know-how."
>
> DAVE RAMSEY

Become Money Smart

You don't have to be a financial or accounting genius to win with money. Financial success isn't reserved just for the select few who actually enjoy running spreadsheets or earn accounting degrees. But you *do* need to be what we call "money smart." That just means you need to understand some basic principles.

» **First**, you need to be comfortable with _____ _____.
₂₄

» **Second**, you must start learning the _____ of money.
₂₅

» **Third**, and this is the hardest part, you need to learn how to manage your _____ with money.
₂₆

Some people make more than $100,000 per year but are living **at survival level** because they spend everything they make (and then some). There are others who make $40,000 per year but live **at a secure level**. How is this possible? **They live on less than they make!**

What Does Winning With Money Look Like?

We can divide financial well-being into three levels.

✱ NOTE: These levels are not determined by income, but rather by how you manage your income.

1. **Survival:** At this level there are simply income, bills and hope that there is enough money to get you to the end of the month. Sounds like fun, right? You work for every dollar you earn and spend everything you earn. This is the living "paycheck to paycheck" level of financial well-being.

2. **Comfort:** At this level, you have a basic understanding of money management. There are still income and bills, however, you pay yourself first! You have a small monthly surplus that you use to save and invest. You are slowly building wealth and moving toward being financially secure.

3. **Secure:** Instead of saving and investing a small surplus, you arrange your finances in such a way that your wealth now generates your income. That's right! At this level, your money actually works for you.

On which level would you like your financial future to rest?

How You View Money Matters

The way we view money is unique and largely dependent on our current financial state. Even though you are still dependent on your parents, you are already developing a "money personality." Some people are really good at saving while others are talented at finding bargains. The fact is we all have strengths and weaknesses; we all have a money personality. How much money a person has, unfortunately, does not always dictate his or her spending behavior. Some millionaires hate spending while some people who are broke can't seem to stop buying things. Money—or the lack of money—can affect the way we feel about ourselves and the way we interact with others. Your relationship with money is complex and dynamic.

» Winning with money isn't just about understanding how it works—it's about putting your _____ into it. That's the 80% behavior we've talked about.

» Money is a _____. It's up to you to manage it.

» The best way to manage money is to learn how to manage _____.

» You need to know your natural _____ when it comes to money. For instance, are you more likely to spend or save?

» Once you know your money _____, you develop a financial plan that works for you.

» It's in recognizing who you really are that allows you the _____ to grow and learn.

Budget Builder

One of the most important steps in winning with money is to have a plan. We are going to teach you how to write a budget. Go to foundationsU.com/1 for your first budget lesson!

During this course, as you develop your knowledge and skills in areas like budgeting and saving, consider your money personality. Think about how your parents and other adults in your life spend and save. Reflect on your own spending habits. Understanding the way you think about money will help you manage your money and make good decisions for your financial future.

JOURNAL QUESTION: VIDEO 3.1

How do you want your financial future to look?

_____

_____

_____

Chapter Summary

 ## Check for Understanding

Now it's time to check your learning! Go back to the Before You Begin section for this chapter. Place a checkmark next to the learning outcomes you've mastered and complete the "after" column of the Measure Your Progress section.

 ## Build On What You've Learned

Fill in the graphic organizer below.

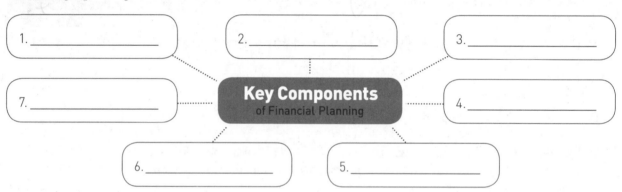

1. _____

2. _____

3. _____

Key Components
of Financial Planning

7. _____

4. _____

6. _____

5. _____

 ## Big Ideas

The following Big Ideas are intended to provide clear focus and purpose to the lessons. Read each statement and think about how what you've learned will affect your current and future decisions. Then, in the space provided, write an "I believe" statement for each of the Big Ideas.

» Personal finance is 80% behavior and 20% head knowledge.

_____

» Many Americans are buried in debt.

_____

» Learn the language of money!

_____

Take Action Challenge

The first key component of financial planning is to assess your current financial situation. This should be pretty easy at your age. It's important to have a clear picture of your income (money in) and expenses (money out) before you move on to the next phases of financial planning. Complete the student financial assessment form below.

LIST ALL INCOME SOURCES

Regular Income Source (job/allowance)	Amount	Pay Period (weekly, biweekly, etc.)
_____	_____	_____
_____	_____	_____

Irregular Income Source (babysitting, summer job, tutoring, etc.)		
_____	_____	N/A

LIST ALL EXPENSES (auto insurance, car payment, cell phone bill, entertainment, clothing, etc.)

Expense	Amount	Pay Period (weekly, biweekly, etc.)
_____	_____	_____
_____	_____	_____
_____	_____	_____
_____	_____	_____
_____	_____	_____

LIST ALL ASSETS (anything you own that has value: car, savings account, etc.)

Asset	Value	
_____	_____	N/A
_____	_____	N/A
_____	_____	N/A
_____	_____	N/A

Money in Review

Matching

Match the following terms to the correct definition below.

A Consumer	**D** Loan	**G** Economy
B Financial Literacy	**E** Debt	**H** Personal Finance
C Credit	**F** Interest	

1. __F__ A fee paid by a borrower to the lender for the use of borrowed money

2. __e__ An obligation of repayment owed by one party (debtor/borrower) to a second party (creditor/lender)

3. __A__ A person or organization that buys/uses goods or services

4. __D__ A debt evidenced by a "note," which specifies the principal amount, interest rate and date of repayment (example: house mortgage)

5. __C__ The granting of a loan and the creation of a debt; any form of deferred payment

6. __G__ A system by which goods and services are produced and distributed

7. __D__ The knowledge and skillset necessary to be an informed consumer and manage finances effectively

8. __H__ All of the decisions and activities of an individual or family regarding their money, including spending, saving, budgeting, etc.

Illustration

Draw a picture representation of each of the following terms.

Money personality	Consumerism

Multiple Choice

Circle the correct answer.

9. Learning the language of money is not that important because you will be able to depend on financial planners to manage your money.

   (A) True   (B) False

10. Which of the following is NOT a reason credit is marketed so heavily to consumers in the United States?

    (A) There is strong consumer demand for big ticket items.

    (B) The credit industry has become extremely profitable.

    (C) The use of credit is not socially accepted in the United States.

    (D) After World War I, credit laws in the United States were relaxed in an attempt to create a mainstream alternative to loan sharks for the working class.

11. During the Great Depression, New Deal policy makers came up with mortgage (home loans) and consumer lending policies that convinced commercial banks that:

    (A) Consumer credit was not a profitable industry.

    (B) Consumer credit could be profitable.

    (C) Consumers would not be willing to use credit, since borrowing money for large purchases had not previously been an option for the middle class.

    (D) They would not be able to compete with loan sharks in the industry of consumer lending.

12. When it comes to managing money, success is about _____% head knowledge and _____% behavior.

    (A) 50, 50   (C) 60, 40

    (B) 80, 20   (D) 20, 80

Short Answer

Respond in the space provided.

13. Describe some of the mistakes Americans often make when it comes to money.

    not saving
    Debt
    n budget

14. Explain why understanding your money personality is important when it comes to developing a money plan that's right for you.

    _____

    _____

    _____

15. Does the History of Credit and Consumerism segment make you view the use of credit differently than you did before? Explain your answer.

    _____

    _____

    _____

16. Explain how marketing can affect your decisions when it comes to spending money.

    buy now
    pay later

17. Does managing your money well mean that you can't have fun with your money? Explain your answer.

    No

    _____

    _____

CHAPTER 2

What do other high school students know about saving?

We asked high school students to describe something they really wanted and thought they *had* to buy, only to realize later that they wasted their money.

....

"I worked and saved $250 for a guitar that I never learned how to play."

Junior, Michigan

"I bought some fish that I thought I really wanted. I never fed them, totally lost interest in them, and they all died. What a waste of money!"

Junior, Alabama

"I really wanted this expensive skateboard that cost $229. I had to have it. Turned out it skated no better than the other ones that were a lot less expensive."

Sophomore, Alabama

"I got a pink Coach purse that I paid more than $200 for and have maybe used twice."

Junior, Florida

"I bought an $80 sweater that turned out to be really cheap quality."

Freshman, Tennessee

Saving

25%

of American families have no savings at all.*

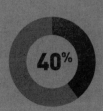

40%

of Americans are not saving for retirement.*

YOU MIGHT BE wondering why you, a teenager, need to worry about saving money. While saving money when you make very little can be a challenge, it is important that you develop a habit of saving a portion of what you earn now. This simple habit can change your life in the years to come. In fact, it's the only foolproof way of becoming a millionaire. The best part is, anyone can do it! The earlier you begin to save, the wealthier you can become—it's as simple as that!

*StatisticBrain.com

Before You Begin

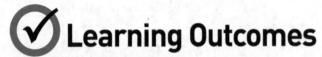 Learning Outcomes

Once you've completed this chapter's videos, you will be asked to return to this list and place a checkmark next to the items you've mastered.

Section 1: Saving: An Exercise of Character

☐ Identify the Five Foundations of personal finance.

☐ Understand the purpose of having an emergency fund.

Section 2: Three Basic Reasons to Save Money

☐ Explain the three basic reasons for saving money.

☐ Understand the importance of saving for both long-term and short-term goals.

☐ Describe what a sinking fund is and identify purchases for which you would use a sinking fund.

Section 3: The Power of Compound Interest

☐ Demonstrate how compound interest works and understand the impact of annual interest rate.

☐ Describe the difference between simple and compound interest.

☐ Understand the importance of beginning to save now.

 Key Terms

Get to know the language of money.

» **Compound interest:** Interest paid on interest previously earned; credited daily, monthly, quarterly or semiannually

» **Emergency fund:** Five hundred dollars in readily available cash to be used only in the event of an emergency; the goal of the First Foundation

» **Interest rate:** Percentage paid to a lender for the use of borrowed money (in debt); percentage earned on invested principal (in investing)

» **Five Foundations:** The five steps to financial success

» **Sinking fund:** Saving money over time for a large purchase

Measure Your Progress

Before watching the video, read each statement below and mark whether you agree or disagree in the "Before" column. Then, after watching the video, do it again using the "After" column to see if you changed your mind on any statement.

BEFORE				AFTER	
Agree	Disagree			Agree	Disagree
☐	☐	1. The amount of money you save depends on how much money you earn. Simply put, you will save more when you earn more.		☐	☐
☐	☐	2. A savings account at your bank is the best place to put your emergency fund.		☐	☐
☐	☐	3. The two biggest factors in compound interest and building wealth are time and the initial amount of the investment.		☐	☐
☐	☐	4. It is okay to use your emergency fund to pay cash for big purchases such as a TV or a cell phone.		☐	☐
☐	☐	5. You should pay yourself first before you pay bills.		☐	☐

JOURNAL QUESTION: INTRODUCTION

What are your initial thoughts about saving? What do you want to learn about saving?

_____

_____

_____

The most important lessons teens want to know when learning how to manage money are learning to save (35%) and understanding how to budget (28%).

ING Direct USA Survey

THE FIVE FOUNDATIONS
are the beginner steps for establishing and maintaining financial peace. These steps will serve as your compass or framework for your financial success. You will find the Five Foundations explained in detail throughout this course. These are basic steps that anyone can and should do in order to win with money. So start now. We want to see you WIN!

CHAPTER 2

Section 1:
Saving: An Exercise of Character

VIDEO 1.1

The Five Foundations

1 THE FIRST FOUNDATION
Save a $500 _Emergicy_ **Fund**

2 THE SECOND FOUNDATION
Get Out of _Debt_

3 THE THIRD FOUNDATION
Pay _Cash_ **for Your Car**

4 THE FOURTH FOUNDATION
Pay Cash for _college_

5 THE FIFTH FOUNDATION
Build _wealth_ **and** _Give_

Saving Money the American Way

THE FIRST FOUNDATION is saving an emergency fund. It is going to rain. Even as a young adult, you need a rainy-day fund. You'll have many financial goals throughout your life. You don't want anything to stand in the way of paying your way through college or buying your first house. But emergencies will happen along the way. *Money Magazine* says that 78% of us will have a major negative event in a given 10-year period of time. At your age, it might be needing to pay for a car repair. Later in life, it might be an extended illness or an injury that keeps you from working for several months. Regardless of the emergency, having money set aside—$500 at your age—will ensure that those life events do not devastate you financially.

 ## Are Americans Good Savers?

A Negative Savings Rate

Back in December 2006, CNN Money reported that Americans had a -0.6% savings rate. The savings rate compares after-tax income to the money people spent on a variety of items. It turns negative when people take on additional debt such as credit cards or car loans. The negative savings rate meant that Americans were spending more money than they were making in 2006. The title of CNN Money's article was "Americans spend every cent and more: Critics say America's negative savings rate can't be sustained and see a recession coming. Are they right?"

Fast Forward to Today

The critics were right, and Americans faced one of the worst recessions in our nation's history.

If our collective spending and saving habits have an effect on the overall economy, shouldn't Americans want to change their behavior? After all, when the economy is strong, we prosper through lower unemployment and higher incomes. When it is weak, we suffer with high unemployment and lower incomes.

Americans' initial response to the economic downturn was positive. In the summer of 2008, the savings rate reached nearly 7%. However, Americans did not maintain this new commitment to saving. By 2010, Americans saved 5.5% of their income. During 2012, that number plunged as low as 3.3%.*

What's the Lesson Here?

When things are good, Americans tend to behave as though things will always be good. The reality is, whether it's an economic downturn or a personal money emergency, you have to be prepared. You need an emergency fund, an old-fashioned rainy-day fund!

*Economic Research, Federal Reserve Bank of St. Louis

The First Foundation

» The First Foundation is $ _500_ in an emergency fund. You should do this as quickly as possible.

» When you're in high school, you won't have the same emergency expenses as your _parents_ (like needing to put a new roof on the house). For you, a surprise expense might be fixing a flat tire or replacing a broken cell phone.

» An emergency fund allows you to have money available for any surprise _emergency_.

» If you don't have money saved to pay for these things, then _loans_ will start looking like an easy answer.

» Debt _doesn't_ solves problems. At best, it just delays one problem while creating another one!

» When you're older and out of school, you'll need to _put_ your emergency fund into a full three to _____ months' worth of expenses.

» Make sure this money is kept in the _bank_ and that you ONLY use it for emergencies. You can't keep the money handy, because it will get spent.

» Keep your emergency fund in a _separate_ savings account away from your spending money.

How Can I Save $500 Quickly?

Five hundred dollars might sound like a lot, but you'd be amazed at how quickly you can pile up some cash! First, make it a goal. Next, set a target date. Goals need a timeline. Now here are some money-making ideas:

1. If you get a regular allowance from your parents, save it! Say goodbye to fancy coffees, vending machine goodies and fast food. Okay, not forever! Those are fun treats. But try limiting yourself to a Friday splurge and saving your money the other days of the week.

2. Hold an auction. Gather things you don't use or need anymore, like expensive clothing or your unused gaming system (get your parents' permission, of course) and sell them online or at a garage sale. You won't believe how much money you have in the form of unused stuff!

3. Become an entrepreneur! Hand out fliers in your neighborhood advertising baby-sitting or yard work services.

4. If you're old enough and your schedule allows it, get a part-time job on the weekends.

5. Communicate your money goals with your parents. They might be willing to pay you for doing extra jobs around the house or for getting good grades.

6. If your parents (or other relatives) own a business, they might be able to hook you up with a part-time job there.

7. Consider tutoring. Some teens report earning as much as $20 an hour.

8. Take advantage of summer months off of school. Explore being a camp counselor, golf caddy or a lifeguard.

9. Watch the local ads for people needing pet sitters or house sitters when they go out of town.

10. Use your skills. Think about what you are good at. You might offer horseback riding lessons, Spanish lessons or piano lessons.

JOURNAL QUESTION: VIDEO 1.1

What has kept you from saving in the past? Based on what you've learned, how can you change this?

_____

_____

_____

80% of America's millionaires are first-generation rich. That means they started with nothing, did smart stuff, and became millionaires.

The Millionaire Next Door

Section 2:
Three Basic Reasons to Save Money

The **First Foundation** is simple. **Save a $500 emergency fund**. Keep in mind that $500 won't always be enough for your emergency fund. As you get older and you have more financial responsibilities like paying a mortgage and supporting a family, you will want to have three to six months of living expenses set aside in your emergency fund. How much money is that? Well, that will depend on what your monthly bills total at any given time. For instance, if your living expenses (mortgage, utilities, insurance, food, etc.) total $3,000 a month, then you'll want to set aside $9,000 to $18,000 in an emergency fund. That sounds like a lot. But rest assured, if you are managing your money wisely, as your income grows so will your savings.

VIDEO 2.1

Save Money for Three Basic Reasons:

1. ___emergency___ Fund 16

2. ___purchase___ 17

3. ___wealth___ Building 18

Emergency Fund

» ___emergency___ are going to happen. Count on it. The First Foundation, a beginner emergency fund, is $500. 19

✱ **NOTE:** Later in life this should increase to three to six months of living expenses.

» It's a good idea to open a separate savings account for your emergency fund. Then, leave it alone!

» Your emergency fund is not an investment. It is insurance for when unexpected things happen.

» The emergency fund is your first savings priority. Do it quickly!

"Save a part of your income and begin now, for the man with a surplus controls circumstances and the man without a surplus is controlled by circumstances."

HENRY BUCKLEY
Australian politician

So now you know about the savings crisis in America. You might be thinking, *Yeah, I'd like to start saving, but I'm barely making any money. And sometimes, doing something fun seems more important than saving just a few bucks. Besides, if I can only save $20 or $50 a month, is it really worth it?*

The Answer: Absolutely! By starting now, you're giving your money time to grow. And when you start young, you'll end up with more cash than someone who waits.

Explain how having an emergency fund helps protect your wealth.

_____

_____

_____

VIDEO 2.2

Purchases

» The second thing you save money for is _purchase_.
[20]

» Instead of _____ to purchase, pay cash by
[21]
using a _____ fund approach.
[22]

A **sinking fund** is a way to save when you know you have a large purchase coming up, like a prom dress or new tires for your car. You calculate the expected cost of the item and how long you have until you need to purchase it. Divide the total cost of the item by the number of months until the purchase. For instance, if prom is five months away and the amount you are willing to spend is $200, you will need to save $40 a month toward your purchase ($200 divided by 5 equals $40).

Saving over time means you will never need to go into debt for a large purchase. Think of it this way: You pay yourself $40 a month, and then pay cash instead of using a credit card and paying someone else $40 a month *plus interest*! That's right. That dress would end up costing you *more than $200* if you borrowed money for it.

In 2012, only **27%** of all point-of-sale purchases were made with cash, and that number is expected to drop to **23%** by 2017.

Report published by Javelin Strategy & Research

WHICH IS WISER?
Using a **sinking fund** versus borrowing money for a large purchase—you make the call.

Say you borrow $4,000 to purchase a dining room set, and your interest rate is 24% for two years.

This means you will have payments of $211 per month for 24 months. So, you will pay a total of $5,064, plus interest, for that set.

But if you use the sinking fund method and save the same $211 per month for only 18 months, you will be able to pay cash.

When you pay cash, you can almost always negotiate a discount. So you will be able to **own** that furniture even earlier for **less money**.

Wealth Building

» The third thing you save money for is
__wealth__ building.

» __saving__ is the key ingredient when it comes to wealth building.

» Building wealth is a __marathon__, not a sprint.

JOURNAL QUESTION: VIDEO 2.2

Why do you think so many people borrow money for large purchases instead of using a sinking fund?

_____

_____

_____

Ready to Start Saving? Read These Bank Tips First!

✱ **REMEMBER:** The emergency fund is not intended to grow wealth, so interest earned is not a factor.

» **A bank is one of the safest places to keep your money.** Since the financial crisis of 2008, the federal government (Federal Deposit Insurance Corporation or FDIC) increased the level of insurance on bank accounts to $250,000 per depositor.

» **An interest-bearing account** is an account that generates interest income on the available balance in the account.

» **The convenience of a bank account comes at a cost.** Banks generally pay lower rates on interest-bearing accounts than other financial institutions that offer accounts that resemble bank services: The most common are brokerage cash management accounts, credit union accounts, and mutual fund money market accounts.

» **Inflation can eat up the interest you earn on an interest-bearing bank account.** Even a low rate of inflation (a persistent rise in the cost of goods and services or the decline in the purchase power of money) generally outpaces what banks pay on interest-bearing accounts.

⏹ Maybe You *Can* Afford That Car!

"I'm 14 and want to buy a car in a couple of years. How much money will it take to get a good one?"

DAVE'S ANSWER: You can buy a good used car for around $3,000. This may seem like a lot right now, but let me show you how easy it can be. Let's say you work part time after school and on weekends. If you make $100 a week and save it all, you'll have enough for a car in only eight months. Pretty cool, huh? Can't do $100 a week? Saving a little bit at a time adds up, and you will eventually reach your goal. Take a look at the graph below for a few ways it can be done.

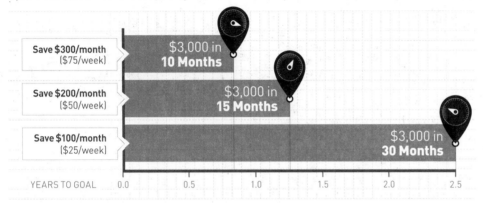

Save $300/month ($75/week) — $3,000 in **10 Months**
Save $200/month ($50/week) — $3,000 in **15 Months**
Save $100/month ($25/week) — $3,000 in **30 Months**

YEARS TO GOAL   0.0   0.5   1.0   1.5   2.0   2.5

VIDEO 2.3

Wealth Building *(Continued)*

» _____ _____ is a mathematical
  26
explosion. You must start _____.
  27

✱ **TURN THE PAGE:** Follow along with the Ben and Arthur compound interest chart to see the power of compound interest!

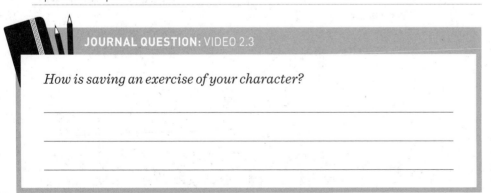

JOURNAL QUESTION: VIDEO 2.3

How is saving an exercise of your character?

_____

_____

_____

IMPORTANT: Since you're in high school, hold off on investing for retirement until you have college completely paid for. It doesn't make sense to invest while, at the same time, taking out loans for college. We want you to live debt free, even through college. Make paying for your education a priority over investing. Once you've done that, invest as soon as possible.

The Story of Ben and Arthur

Both save $2,000 per year at 12%. Ben starts at age 19 and stops at age 26, while Arthur starts at age 27 and stops at age 65.

Ben invested
ONLY $16,000.

Ben stops investing;
Arthur starts investing

Saving $2,000 each
year works out to
only $167 per month!

$2,000 INVESTED ANNUALLY
÷ 12 MONTHS
$167 INVESTED MONTHLY

Arthur
invested
$78,000 and
**NEVER
CAUGHT UP!**

Ben came out
ahead by over
$700,000!

	BEN		Age	ARTHUR	
Invests	Running Total			Invests	Running Total
2,000	2,240		19	0	0
2,000	4,749		20	0	0
2,000	7,558		21	0	0
2,000	10,706		22	0	0
2,000	14,230		23	0	0
2,000	18,178		24	0	0
2,000	22,599		25	0	0
2,000	27,551		26	0	0
0	30,857		27	2,000	2,240
0	34,560		28	2,000	4,749
0	38,708		29	2,000	7,558
0	43,352		30	2,000	10,706
0	48,554		31	2,000	14,230
0	54,381		32	2,000	18,178
0	60,907		33	2,000	22,599
0	68,216		34	2,000	27,551
0	76,802		35	2,000	33,097
0	85,570		36	2,000	39,309
0	95,383		37	2,000	46,266
0	107,339		38	2,000	54,058
0	120,220		39	2,000	62,785
0	134,646		40	2,000	72,559
0	150,804		41	2,000	83,506
0	168,900		42	2,000	95,767
0	189,168		43	2,000	109,499
0	211,869		44	2,000	124,879
0	237,293		45	2,000	142,104
0	265,768		46	2,000	161,396
0	297,660		47	2,000	183,004
0	333,379		48	2,000	207,204
0	373,385		49	2,000	234,308
0	418,191		50	2,000	264,665
0	468,374		51	2,000	298,665
0	524,579		52	2,000	336,745
0	587,528		53	2,000	379,394
0	658,032		54	2,000	427,161
0	736,995		55	2,000	480,660
0	825,435		56	2,000	540,579
0	924,487		57	2,000	607,688
0	1,035,425		58	2,000	682,851
0	1,159,676		59	2,000	767,033
0	1,298,837		60	2,000	861,317
0	1,454,698		61	2,000	966,915
0	1,629,261		62	2,000	1,085,185
0	1,824,773		63	2,000	1,217,647
0	2,043,746		64	2,000	1,366,005
0	2,288,996		65	2,000	1,532,166

Grand Total → **$2,288,996** vs **$1,532,166**

Section 3:
The Power of Compound Interest

VIDEO 3.1: THERE ARE NO FILL-INS IN THIS SECTION.

What Is Interest?

> *The most powerful force in the universe is compound interest!"*
> ALBERT EINSTEIN, German physicist

What is **interest**? In investing, it is the money the principal (original amount invested) earns. It is typically a percentage of the principal, paid on a monthly, quarterly or annual basis.

Compound interest is interest paid on interest previously earned.

Whew! Need further explanation? Here's an example.

Take a one-time investment of $1,000 and earn 10% on it. Your interest earned at the end of the year is $100.

Add that to your original $1,000, and you have $1,100.

At the end of the next year, your $1,100 is compounded at 10% interest, so your return on investment is $110. Add that to the $1,100, and you now have $1,210. Your interest on $1,210 is $121.

So as time passes, the amount you earn from interest grows. That is why it is so important that you start as early as possible. You have more time for your interest to snowball and pick up more and more snow!

How to Calculate Compound Interest

Use this simple formula to figure out the future value of a deposit once compound interest has worked its magic.

$$FV = PV \left(1 + r/m\right)^{mt}$$

---

* REMEMBER: When calculating this formula, use the mathematical order of operations.

FV: The future value
PV: The present value
r: The annual rate of interest as a decimal (5% is expressed as the decimal 0.05)

m: The number of times per year the interest is compounded (monthly, annually, etc.)
t: The number of years you leave it invested

INTERESTED IN INVESTING?
We will talk more about investing in Chapter 8.

What excites you most about investing?

"Making money without doing anything."
Junior, Oklahoma

"Being able to be financially secure when I retire."
Senior, Florida

"I am excited about what even a small investment can become."
Senior, Colorado

"Having tons of money in the end."
Senior, New Jersey

"Patience is golden because it will increase the satisfaction you take from achieving your goals and desires."

DAVE RAMSEY

Budget Builder

Saving money is a lot easier to do when you make it part of your budget! Go to foundationsU.com/2 for your next budget lesson.

See what your investment will be worth in 40 years! Check out the Investing Calculator at foundationsU.com.

Compound Interest *(Continued)*

Inflation: Inflation is a persistent rise in the price of goods and services over a period of time.

Time Value of Money: This principle suggests that a certain amount of money today has different buying power than the same amount of money in the future. This notion exists both because there is an opportunity to earn interest on the money and because inflation will drive prices up, thereby changing the "value" of the money.

So let's say you and a friend each get $100 for your birthdays. Your friend buys designer jeans, and you put your cash in a savings account. In two years, your money will have earned interest. But will you have enough cash to buy the same designer jeans?

The trade-off between money now and money later depends on, among other things, the inflation rate and the rate of interest you can earn by investing or saving.

The rate of return, or the interest rate, on your investment is important to consider. We will talk about different types of investments and rate of return in detail in Chapter 8, *Investing and Retirement.*

📊 How Important Is My Interest Rate?

Look at what happens to a $1,000 one-time investment with no withdrawals from age 25 to age 65 (40 years).

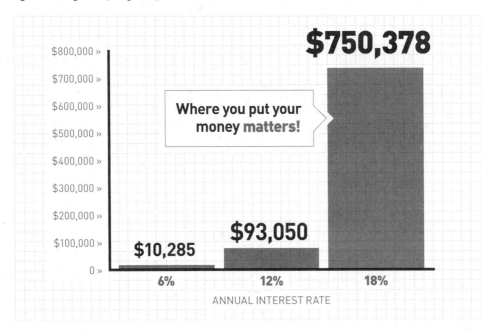

$800,000 »
$700,000 »
$600,000 »
$500,000 »
$400,000 »
$300,000 »
$200,000 »
$100,000 »
0 »

Where you put your money matters!

$750,378

$93,050

$10,285

6%   **12%**   **18%**

ANNUAL INTEREST RATE

JOURNAL QUESTION: VIDEO 3.1

Why don't more people save for the future? Which reasons can be fixed by having a money plan?

_____

_____

_____

> *"Most people have the will to win; few have the will to prepare to win."*
>
> **BOBBY KNIGHT**
> Former head coach of the Indiana Hoosiers (1971–2000)

Chapter Summary

 ## Check for Understanding

Now it's time to check your learning! Go back to the Before You Begin section for this chapter. Place a checkmark next to the learning outcomes you've mastered and complete the "after" column of the Measure Your Progress section.

 ## Build On What You've Learned

Review: The Three Reasons to Save

Fill in the graphic organizer. What are the three things you need to save for? Describe why each is important for your financial future. Take a look at section 2 if you need help.

3 Reasons to Save

1

SAVE FOR:
_____

IMPORTANT BECAUSE:
_____
_____
_____
_____
_____

2

SAVE FOR:
_____

IMPORTANT BECAUSE:
_____
_____
_____
_____
_____

3

SAVE FOR:
_____

IMPORTANT BECAUSE:
_____
_____
_____
_____
_____

⚡ Take Action Challenge

See how quickly you can save your $500 emergency fund. Set a time goal and make it happen!

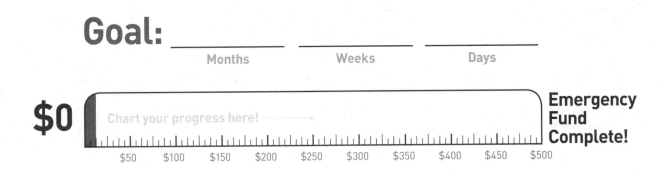

Goal: _____ _____ _____
        Months   Weeks   Days

$0 | Chart your progress here! ·····················►
    $50 $100 $150 $200 $250 $300 $350 $400 $450 $500

Emergency Fund Complete!

💡 Big Ideas

The following Big Ideas are intended to provide clear focus and purpose to the lessons. Read each statement and think about how what you've learned will affect your current and future decisions. Then, in the space provided, write an "I believe" statement for each of the Big Ideas.

» The Five Foundations are your steps to Financial Peace.

_____

» The First Foundation: Save a $500 Emergency Fund

_____

» Save for emergencies, large purchases and wealth building.

_____

Money in Review

Matching

Match the following terms to the correct definition below.

Ⓐ The Five Foundations   Ⓓ Compound Interest   Ⓖ Interest-Bearing Account

Ⓑ Interest Rate   Ⓔ Emergency Fund

Ⓒ Sinking Fund   Ⓕ Inflation

1. _____ An account that generates interest income on the available balance in the account

2. _____ The five steps to financial success

3. _____ A savings account that is set aside to be used only for emergency expenses

4. _____ Interest paid on interest previously earned

5. _____ Saving money over time for a large purchase

6. _____ A rate which is either charged (on debt) or paid (on investment accounts) for the use of money

7. _____ The persistent increase in the cost of goods and services or the persistent decline in the purchasing power of money

Illustration

Draw a picture representation of each of the following terms.

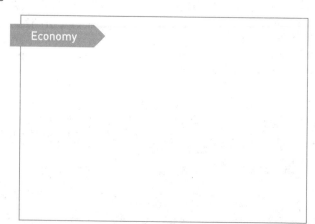

Recession

Economy

Multiple Choice

Circle the correct answer.

8. When it comes to saving money, the amount you save is determined by how much you have left at the end of the month once all of your spending is done.
    - Ⓐ True
    - Ⓑ False

9. Your income level greatly affects your saving habits.
    - Ⓐ True
    - Ⓑ False

10. At your age, a fully funded emergency fund should be:
    - Ⓐ $1,000
    - Ⓑ $5,000
    - Ⓒ $100
    - Ⓓ $500

11. Which of the following is not one of the three basic reasons for saving money?
    - Ⓐ Large purchases
    - Ⓑ Have money available to lend to friends
    - Ⓒ Emergency fund
    - Ⓓ Build wealth

12. Instead of borrowing money for large purchases, you should set money aside in a _____ over time and pay with cash.
    - Ⓐ Sinking fund
    - Ⓑ Emergency fund
    - Ⓒ Credit card fund
    - Ⓓ Mortgage fund

Short Answer

Respond in the space provided.

13. What is the First Foundation? Explain how and why the dollar amount will change as you get older.

_____

_____

_____

14. Looking back at the "Ben and Arthur" story, how did Ben come out ahead even though he invested less money than Arthur?

_____

_____

_____

15. What two things do you consider when evaluating the time value of money?

_____

_____

_____

16. Calculate the compound interest for each problem below.
    - $1,000 at 6% interest for three years

    _____
    - $500 at 18% interest for four years

    _____
    - $1,500 at 12% interest for two years

    _____

17. Why do you need an emergency fund at your age?

_____

_____

_____

CHAPTER 3

What do other high school students know about budgeting?

We asked high school students to share some tips on how to handle money.

....

"Put yourself on a budget and be wise with your money. That way you won't be tempted to dip into your savings account."

Freshman, Florida

"Get direct deposit and put money right into your savings account. Then only spend the money you have left over."

Senior, Missouri

"It's a good idea to start saving with your first paycheck because once you start spending, it is hard to stop."

Junior, Tennessee

"Expenses don't just happen— they're always there. It takes practice to save money and not spend it all."

Junior, Utah

"It is good to make a money plan. You should save a percentage every month, even if it is not a lot."

Freshman, Texas

Budgeting

56%

of U.S. adults admit that they do not have a budget.*

33%

of Americans do not pay all of their bills on time. That's more than 77 million people!*

BECOMING WEALTHY DOESN'T happen accidentally. It is a journey that requires intentionality, persistence and discipline. But with all of life's distractions, how can you stay focused on your money goals? A budget is the perfect solution. It's simple—just write down a plan for your money and intentionally follow it every day. Surprisingly, when you put boundaries on your spending, you end up with more freedom!

*National Foundation for Credit Counseling, Inc.

Before You Begin

✓ Learning Outcomes

Once you've completed this chapter's videos, you will be asked to return to this list of learning outcomes and place a checkmark next to the items you've mastered.

Section 1: Budgeting 101

☐ Understand the purpose of cash flow planning.

☐ Identify reasons some people avoid having or sticking to a budget.

☐ Identify changes in personal spending behavior that contribute to wealth building.

☐ Explain the difference between a cash flow statement and a budget.

Section 2: The Basics of Banking

☐ Develop a filing system for keeping financial records, both paper and electronic.

☐ Describe recordkeeping features that financial institutions provide for online account management.

☐ Describe how to use different payment methods and banking features.

Section 3: The Importance of Having a Zero-Based Budget

☐ Define zero-based budget.

☐ Develop a plan for spending and saving that has both long-term and short-term components.

☐ Analyze how changes in circumstances can affect a personal budget.

Key Terms

Get to know the language of money.

» **Budget:** A written cash flow plan

» **Cash Flow Statement:** A summary that shows total income and spending for a given time period

» **Carbon Check:** A copy of each check you write

» **Envelope System:** Series of envelopes that are divided into categories (food, entertainment, gas, etc.) and are used to store cash for planned monthly expenses

» **Impulse Purchase:** An item that is bought without previous planning or consideration of the long-term effects

» **Overdraft:** Occurs when money is withdrawn from a bank account and the available balance goes below zero

» **Reconcile:** To match your bank statement with your checkbook

» **Zero-Based Budget:** A cash flow plan that assigns an expense to every dollar of your income, wherein the total income minus the total expenses equals zero

Measure Your Progress

Before watching the video, read each statement below and mark whether you agree or disagree in the "Before" column. Then, after watching the video, do it again using the "After" column to see if you changed your mind on any statement.

BEFORE			AFTER	
Agree	Disagree		Agree	Disagree
☐	☐	1. It is important to know how to live within my means and have good money habits.	☐	☐
☐	☐	2. I expect and would like my parents to stop supporting me before age 25.	☐	☐
☐	☐	3. I am knowledgeable about money management, including budgeting and saving.	☐	☐
☐	☐	4. I am prepared to deal with the adult financial world after school.	☐	☐
☐	☐	5. I know how to balance and reconcile my checking account.	☐	☐
☐	☐	6. I know how to write a check.	☐	☐
☐	☐	7. I have more than $100 in savings.	☐	☐

JOURNAL QUESTION: INTRODUCTION

On average, how much money do you spend per week? $_____

What are your top three expenses?

1. _____

2. _____

3. _____

CHAPTER 3

> "If you will happen to your money, then you'll have some. If you just let all your money happen to you, then you'll never win."
>
> DAVE RAMSEY

10 THINGS MILLIONAIRES DO NOT DO

1. Buy brand-new cars
2. Eat out on a regular basis
3. Replace what is not broken
4. Impulse buy
5. Carry debt
6. Visit the tanning bed
7. Buy brand-name clothes
8. Desire instant gratification
9. Socialize with people who waste money
10. Spend more money than they earn

The Millionaire Next Door

Section 1: Budgeting 101

VIDEO 1.1

Cash Flow Planning

BUDGETING IS CRUCIAL to your success. Your income is your responsibility. If you get to retirement with a mountain of debt and nothing to live on, it's no one else's fault. But beyond the obvious financial benefits of managing your money well, there are a ton of other reasons to pull out the budget forms every month. It may sound nerdy or old fashioned, but it isn't. Keeping a budget is really helpful for everyone. A simple, written plan can actually give you more money to enjoy!

» Money is _____. It is moving all the time. So if you don't make your money behave, you'll always wonder where it went.

» You must do a written _____ _____ plan every _____. A budget is your blueprint for building wealth. You've got to have a game plan!

» A budget might seem intimidating at first, but it is not as intimidating as going broke!

✱ **REMEMBER:** Don't try to have the perfect budget for the perfect month, because you'll never have one. A good cash flow plan lives and moves—it changes as your life changes.

Describe in your own words what it means to have a budget.

_____

_____

_____

VIDEO 1.2

Four Reasons People Avoid Budgets

Doing a budget or cash flow plan doesn't sound like much fun. In fact, people will come up with lots of excuses for not keeping a budget.

1. It has a _____ connotation. They believe that having a budget will constrict them and keep them from doing what they want to do. The reality is, managed money goes further and actually gives you more freedom.

2. A budget has been used to _____ them. They're constantly hearing, "It's not in the budget!" The purpose of a budget is to not spend more than you make. It is not intended to take all the fun out of your life.

3. They've never had a budget that _____. Don't expect to write a perfect budget on your first try. You will make mistakes. With some practice, however, writing a monthly budget will become easier.

"There are plenty of ways to get ahead. The first is so basic I'm almost embarrassed to say it: Spend less than you earn."

PAUL CLITHEROE
Australian financial advisor

WHAT'S THE DIFFERENCE BETWEEN A CASH FLOW STATEMENT AND A BUDGET?
A cash flow statement summarizes all of the income and outgo (spending) over a certain time period. A budget is a written plan for saving, giving and spending. The cash flow statement is reflective of what has already taken place, and a budget is a proactive plan of what will take place.

"People don't plan to fail, they fail to plan."

ANONYMOUS

DESCRIBE SOME STRENGTHS AND WEAKNESSES YOU HAVE WHEN IT COMES TO MANAGING MONEY.

"I don't spend money on stupid things. But when I have more money, I tend to spend more."
Senior, Oregon

"One of my strengths is saving short term and not getting into debt. One of my weaknesses is buying things I don't need."
Sophomore, New York

Four Reasons People Avoid Budgets *(Continued)*

4. Paralysis from ________ of what they will find. Some people are afraid to look at their finances closely. It's better to face those bills or debts and begin to proactively fix the situation. Ignoring financial distress only allows the problem to get bigger.

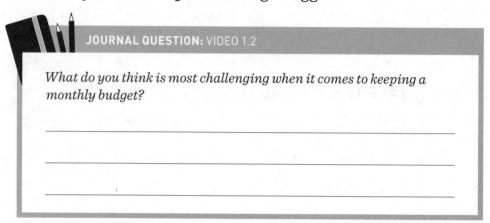

JOURNAL QUESTION: VIDEO 1.2

What do you think is most challenging when it comes to keeping a monthly budget?

____

____

____

Real Wealth Building Begins With Your Behavior

Often the importance of smart money-management techniques gets overlooked. Why is it important to manage your money well? What impact does managing money well have on your long-term financial well-being? Studies show that simple changes in your spending and saving habits will help you build wealth.

1. Live on less than you make. Don't spend every dollar of your paycheck.

2. Keep on learning and finding ways to grow your income.

3. Write a monthly budget that includes saving, giving and spending. Stick to it.

4. Plan your spending and avoid impulse or unnecessary purchases.

5. Stay out of debt.

6. Pay yourself first. This means assigning a portion of your income to saving and investing every month.

7. Use gifts and "extra" income wisely. You might be tempted to just blow money you receive as a gift. It's okay to use some of that money to treat yourself to a "want." But it's wise to use a portion of it toward a money goal (like getting out of debt, saving for a car, saving for college, etc.).

Section 2: The Basics of Banking

Responsible Banking

Managing your money will involve banking. Once you've established cash flow, either through employment or an allowance from your parents, you should open a checking account. Don't forget about your First Foundation: Save a $500 emergency fund. This money should be placed in a separate savings account. You should consider your checking account as your spending account and always keep your savings separate.

Learning how to keep your checking account balanced is an important and necessary skill.

» You must keep your checking account _____. Keeping an accurate balance of your checking account will help you avoid the most frequent and costly mistake, the overdraft. Each occurrence can cost an average of $35 for the bounced check fee at your bank, plus possible store charges.

» _____ are a sign of crisis living and sloppy, lazy _____ habits. Remember, managing your money is your responsibility. Managing money well is a sign of maturity.

» Use _____, or carbon checks, if necessary to keep up with your check register. Just looking at your online statement every few days to see how much money is in the account is not enough. Your online statement may not reflect unprocessed checks or debit purchases.

» If not managed and made to behave, the _____ card is certain to become a budget buster.

"This is your wealth we're talking about here! Get excited! Make those dollars dance!"

DAVE RAMSEY

It's important to know how much things cost before you buy. A smart doctor once wrote, "Suppose one of you wants to build a tower. What is the first thing you will do? Won't you sit down and figure out how much it will cost and if you have enough money to pay for it? Otherwise, you will start building the tower, but not be able to finish. Then everyone who sees what is happening will laugh at you. They will say, 'You started building, but could not finish the job'". (Luke 14:28–30).

"Every young man should have a hobby. Learning how to handle money is the best one."

JACK HURLEY
Boxing manager and trainer

Balancing Your Checking Account

At first, keeping track of your transactions may seem tedious and unnecessary. But once you get the hang of it, balancing a checking account is actually easy. By keeping track, you can avoid a bunch of headaches, like bouncing a check, the bank making mistakes with your account, or not knowing your actual balance. Remember, when you take responsibility for your money, you'll have more of it!

What You'll Need

1. **Your Check Register** or **Smartphone Budgeting App**

2. **Your Last Bank Statement** or **Online Account Summary**

3. **A Reconciliation Sheet** (on the back of most bank statements or you can find one online)

Things to Remember

» If you were diligent with recording transactions in your check register every time money went in or out, your check register has the most current balance.

» Remember, the account balance from the bank statement or ATM is not as current as your register's balance because they don't account for transactions that haven't gone through yet.

» Contact the bank if you think they made an error. It happens more than you may think.

» Don't be discouraged on the first few tries. Balancing your account takes practice. The more you do it, the easier it becomes.

How to Do It

» Throughout the month, write down every deposit or withdrawal in your register. Your transactions might include ATM withdrawals, checks you've written, debit card purchases, bank fees and paychecks.

» Each time you make an entry in your register, add or subtract that amount from the current balance.

» When you receive your monthly bank statement, record any interest accrual and bank fees in the check register.

Compare Your Check Register and Bank Statement Side by Side

» Compare each transaction one by one. As you do this, make checkmarks on both lists.

» On the reconciliation sheet, list any debits or deposits that are present in the register but not present in the bank statement. Then calculate those into your bank statement balance.

» Compare your register balance to the statement balance. They should be the same. If not, look for discrepancies like outstanding checks, unrecorded bank fees or transactions, or bank errors.

Check Register / Smartphone Budgeting App

✓	Trans. #	Date	Transaction Description	Payment (-)	Deposit (+)	Balance
	5671	8/12	One Stop Grocery	57.40		507.06
	5672	8/14	Electric Company	101.00		406.06
		8/14	Paycheck		700.00	1106.06
	5673	8/16	Telephone Company	50.00		1056.06
	5674	8/19	One Stop Grocery	66.00		990.06
		8/16	Bank Service Charge	2.50		$987.56

◀ Starting balance of $564.46

Bank Statement

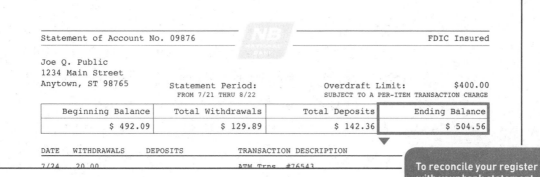

Statement of Account No. 09876   FDIC Insured

Joe Q. Public
1234 Main Street
Anytown, ST 98765   Statement Period: Overdraft Limit: $400.00
                            FROM 7/21 THRU 8/22   SUBJECT TO A PER-ITEM TRANSACTION CHARGE

Beginning Balance	Total Withdrawals	Total Deposits	Ending Balance
$ 492.09	$ 129.89	$ 142.36	$ 504.56

DATE   WITHDRAWALS   DEPOSITS   TRANSACTION DESCRIPTION

7/24   20.00   ATM Trns #76543

To reconcile your register with your bank statement, start with the ending balance from your statement.

Reconciliation Sheet

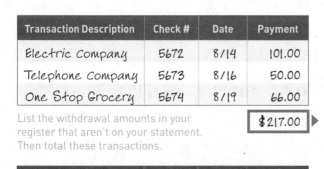

Transaction Description	Check #	Date	Payment
Electric Company	5672	8/14	101.00
Telephone Company	5673	8/16	50.00
One Stop Grocery	5674	8/19	66.00

List the withdrawal amounts in your register that aren't on your statement. Then total these transactions. $217.00 ▶

Transaction Description	Check #	Date	Deposit
Paycheck		8/14	700.00

List the deposit amounts in your register that aren't on your statement. Then total these transactions. $700.00 ▶

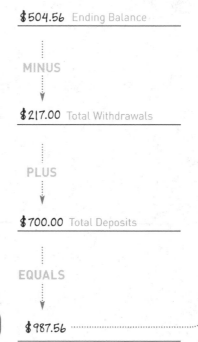

$504.56 Ending Balance

MINUS

$217.00 Total Withdrawals

PLUS

$700.00 Total Deposits

EQUALS

This should be the same as your register balance.

$987.56

Keep Records

» Smart money managers develop a filing system for keeping and using financial records. You should maintain both paper and electronic files for reference.

» These records will be useful for filing taxes and for disputing bank errors or fraudulent purchases.

» You may want to check with your bank to find out what online record keeping features they offer.

» In this digital age, it's easy to personalize a system that works for you. Explore phone apps and software that may help in many areas of personal finance like budgeting, saving and keeping records.

Are Multiple Accounts a Good Idea?

"I just got a part-time job, and I want to make sure I save some money in case something bad happens to my car. Do you think I should tell my parents I want to open a checking account and a savings account?"

DAVE'S ANSWER: First, congratulations on the new job! You've taken a big first step toward financial independence.

Second, I think it's a great idea to keep your checking and savings accounts separate, and here's why. If you put all your money in one place,

it becomes too easy to dip into your savings or emergency fund when you're writing checks. This defeats the original purpose of saving money.

This separation acts as a mental note and a barrier. It's a way of telling you that you've reached your spending limit!

Banking Tools

Writing Checks

Checks can be used to pay bills at a store, give a person a check if you are short of cash, or send a check through the mail or electronically. Checks allow you to pay for things without having to carry large amounts of cash. Most stores will want some basic information if you are using a check, such as your address and phone number, and most will require you to show a photo ID.

Online Bill Pay

Online bill pay allows you to make payments without having to write a check and send it in the mail. After logging into your bank's online site, you can specify whom you want to pay and how much. Your bank will either make an electronic transfer or mail a check to satisfy the payment. A great benefit of using online bill pay is the option to schedule repeat payments.

Debit Card Purchases (In Store and Online)

A debit card can be used for both in-store and online purchases. Although your debit card may have a credit card logo on it, it is not a credit card. When used, money is withdrawn from your checking account for the purchase. We recommend selecting the "credit" option instead of "debit" when making a store purchase. While the funds are withdrawn from your account in the same way, using the credit option ensures that you are protected by the card company's zero-liability policy. You will not be responsible for unauthorized transactions. If you do decide to use your PIN, be sure to memorize your PIN and never carry it with you.

Account Transfers

Account transfers allow you to move money between your accounts. Once you have a regular income, we recommend setting up weekly or monthly automatic transfers from your checking to your savings account. This is the easiest way to build your savings for emergency fund or large purchases.

FIRST CHECKING ACCOUNT?

Make it free checking. There are plenty of $0 monthly fee accounts out there. You may want to open your first account at your parents' bank in order to take advantage of special multi-account privileges. Either way, shop around to get an account with minimal or no fees.

WHAT TEENS SHOULD KNOW ABOUT DEBIT CARDS

- Keep them secure at all times.
- Pick a secure PIN (personal identification number).
- Trust your friends, but not with your debit card!
- Be cautious of online transactions. Reconciling your account will help you be aware of fraudulent charges.

Banking Tools *(Continued)*

ATM

The ATM (automatic teller machine) allows you to make withdrawals, deposits or transfers without entering your bank. Normally your bank will not charge you an ATM fee when you use their ATMs. But be aware that if you use an ATM owned by another bank, you will be charged a fee for your withdrawal, usually from both your bank and the competitor.

Mobile Banking

Mobile banking takes a lot of the features of online banking and brings them to your cell or smartphone. They may also offer additional features like text alerts and text banking. Mobile banking features will vary from bank to bank.

JOURNAL QUESTION: VIDEO 2.1

Explain why Dave describes overdrafts as a sign of "crisis living."

_____

_____

_____

FOUR TYPES OF EXPENSES TO BUDGET FOR

Variable Expenses: Expenses that vary from month to month (e.g., electricity, gasoline, groceries, clothing)

Fixed Expenses: Expenses that remain the same from month to month (e.g., rent, insurance premiums, cable bill)

Intermittent Expenses: Expenses that occur at various times throughout the year and tend to be in large lump sums (e.g., tuition payments, athletic or club dues, car repairs)

Discretionary (Non-Essential) Expenses: Expenses for things we don't need (e.g., eating out, gifts and candy)

Section 3: The Importance of Having a Zero-Based Budget

VIDEO 3.1

Cash Flow Plans Do Not Work When . . .

» You _____ things _____. Make sure your budget includes everything that requires money. You may forget and leave some things out at first, but as you get better at budgeting, that will happen less frequently.

» You _____ your plan. All you really need is paper, a pen and a calculator. It's as simple as writing down everything that requires money each month and putting an amount next to it.

» You don't actually _____ _____. This may sound overly simple, but it's easy to find reasons not to write a budget. When this happens, remind yourself of all the reasons you should do it.

» You don't actually _____ on it. Your written plan will not work unless you actually follow it. And as you get used to it, you may see some budget items that aren't realistic. That's okay! Just adjust the budget for next month until you get it right.

THINK A CREDIT CARD IS SAFER TO USE THAN A DEBIT CARD?
Think again. Some people believe that credit cards carry a better track record and that you're less likely to have your money stolen when you use a credit card. Sadly, those people are wrong.

Credit cards carry a huge risk of allowing the user to incur debt. Debit cards force you to pay with money you already have. If you hold a debit card from a well-known name like Visa or MasterCard, it will have the same policy about unauthorized charges that credit cards have. Don't fool yourself into thinking that credit cards are the "safe" way to go. They'll only get you into trouble and force you to make payments.

Reasons You Should Do a Cash Flow Plan

» A written plan removes the "management by _____ " from your finances. Seventy percent of Americans are living paycheck to paycheck, just one missed payday away from disaster. [18]

» _____ money goes further. That's because when you write up a budget, you're accounting for every single dollar of your income. You cut out all of those little expenses that fly into your wallet like moths and eat away at your money. [19]

Money Affects Relationships

Consider your future relationship. The number-one cause of strife in marriage today is money. It's disagreements over debt. It's disagreements over the stress that debt brings. It's not agreeing on what we're going to purchase and where we're going to spend the money we make. When you are not on the same page with money, you are not on the same page in life.

» A written plan, if actually lived and agreed on, will remove many of the _____ _____ in a relationship. [20]

» A written plan, if actually lived and agreed on, will remove much of the _____, _____ and _____ that may be part of buying necessities such as food or clothing. [21] [22] [23]

» A written plan, if actually lived and agreed on, will remove many of the _____ from your life, consequently removing a lot of _____. [24] [25]

» A written plan, if actually lived and agreed on, will show if you are _____ in a certain area. [26]

43% of parents review bank statements with their kids monthly.

Only 28% of children have used online banking to view their savings account balance.

National Foundation for Credit Counseling, Inc.

HAVE YOU EVER WITNESSED MONEY AFFECTING A RELATIONSHIP CLOSE TO YOU?

"Yes. My dad and mom have been struggling a lot financially. I think it affects their relationship."
Junior, Colorado

"Yes. My mom and stepdad's relationship is constantly strained due to lack of money."
Senior, Georgia

How Do You Budget With Irregular Income?

"I baby-sit from time to time for a neighbor. How do I do a budget when I don't know how much money I'll make each month?"

DAVE'S ANSWER: First, make a list of all of your expenses for the month ahead. Write down absolutely everything that you'll need or want to spend money on. This includes everything from rent to gas to savings to weekend fun money. Write it all down.

Then, prioritize the list in order of importance. Ask yourself, "If I only have enough to pay for one thing, what would it be?" That's number one. Then ask, "If I only have enough to pay for one more thing,

what would it be?" That's number two. Keep that up all the way down the list.

Now you're ready to get paid! When your check comes in, just spend your money all the way down the list. When the money's gone, you're done spending for the month. That's why it is so important to prioritize the list. You may not have enough cash for everything you want to do each month, so make sure you're making the best with what you have.

JOURNAL QUESTION: VIDEO 3.1

Why do you think it is so common in America to spend more than you make?

_____

_____

_____

IRREGULAR INCOME
Shaun sells real estate and has what we call an "irregular income." That just means his income fluctuates from month to month. If you're in this situation, you absolutely must do a monthly budget, but you'll do it a little differently.

Budget Builder

It's time to evaluate what you spend money on and put it in your budget. Spending money is a lot more fun when you plan for it first. Go to foundationsU.com/3 for your next budget lesson.

51% of parents give their children allowance, but only 4% require them to deposit that money into a bank account.

38% of parents match their children's savings.

National Foundation for Credit Counseling, Inc.

VIDEO 3.2

The Zero-Based Budget

» The zero-based budget gives every dollar a name on paper, on purpose, _____ the month begins. This is the best method of budgeting since it ensures that every dollar you make is assigned a specific purpose. Money that is not directed toward a goal or included in a plan is typically wasted.

» Income minus outgo equals exactly _____. This way you are able to put every dollar to work for you.

» The _____ _____ works great for managing spending on things that don't normally have a fixed monthly expense, like eating out. Decide how much you have to spend on each specific category and place that amount in an envelope. When the envelope for a specific area of spending—like clothing or entertainment—is empty, you are done spending in that area for the month.

The Student Budget Form

» Think you don't have money to budget? You've got some _____, you just need to think a little differently.

» If you have a part-time _____ after school or even if your parents give you a commission for doing _____ around the house, you've got some money.

» But it goes further than that. If your parents buy you clothes or give you money to go out with your friends, pay for club or athletic fees, or put gas in your car, all of those things represent _____ that are flowing right through your fingers.
  33

» All we want you to do is _____ how you're going to spend that money _____ you actually spend it. That's all a budget is!
  34   35

» Instead of having your parents pay for stuff, ask if they'll figure out how much money they'd end up giving you for the month and then put it in your _____ account. From there, it will be up to you to budget that money.
  36

» If your folks go along with this, then you'll have a pile of money to _____ every month.
  37

» We've developed a _____ budget form just for you. So no more _____! Starting this month, you will do a written budget every month for the rest of your life!
  38   39

JOURNAL QUESTION: VIDEO 3.2

Explain in your own words what a zero-based budget is. Why is it important to write a zero-based budget every month?

_____

_____

_____

YOUR BUDGET WILL ONLY WORK IF YOU FOLLOW IT.
Here are three tips to help you stick to a budget.

1. **Write it down.** A budget is not a form of medieval torture! It is YOUR game plan, where YOU tell YOUR money what YOU want it to do. This isn't rocket science! Just give every dollar a name on paper.

2. **Stay away from places that tempt you to spend.** If you have a problem sticking to a budget, you may not yet be disciplined. If that's the case, stay out of the mall or wherever your spending weakness occurs.

3. **Use the envelope system.** Take some envelopes, write your budget categories on the envelopes, and use only that money to purchase those items. Try only a couple of categories at first until you get the hang of it. If the money is not in there, you can't spend it. Easy as pie. And remember, it takes practice; you won't get it right the first time.

The Student Budget

Yes, this budget form has a lot of lines and blanks. But that's okay. We do that so we can list practically every expense imaginable on this form to prevent you from forgetting something. Don't expect to put something on every line. Just use the ones that are relevant to your specific situation. Now follow the steps below to get started!

1 Add Up Your Monthly Income

Write your monthly income in the box at the bottom of the page (**A**), including any money your parents give you. This is the amount you have to spend for the month. Pretty simple, right?

2 Estimate Your Spending

Within each category, like **RECREATION**, there are items like Movies and Sporting Events. Start at the top and work your way down, filling out the Budgeted column (**B**) first. Then add up each subcategory and put that number in each category's Total box (e.g., **C**).

✴ **REMEMBER:** Your spending will change from month to month. Just put a "$0" in categories where you don't plan on spending any money.

✴ **NOTE:** The envelope icons (✉) represent good options for cash envelopes.

3 Total Each Category

Go through the form and add up all of the category Total boxes (e.g., **C**). Write that grand total in the Monthly Outgo box (**D**). That's how much you spend every month.

The goal is to spend every dollar you make, but no more. So if your Outgo is greater than your Income, you need to bring down the budgeted amount on some items. If your Outgo is less than your Income, you need to increase the amount in some area like College savings or Restaurants.

4 Get to Zero

Once your Outgo is the same as your Income, write a zero in the Zero box at the bottom (**E**). You're done!

Start Here

To begin your journey toward financial success!

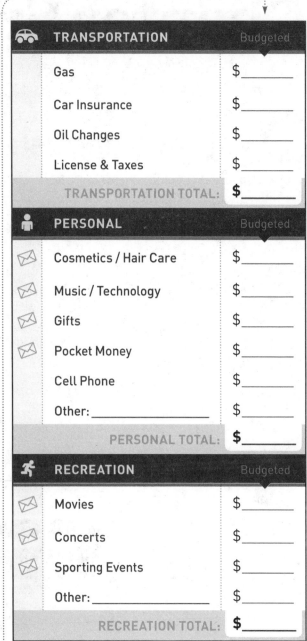

GIVING	Ⓑ Budgeted
Charity	$_____
Other: _____	$_____
Ⓒ GIVING TOTAL:	$_____

SAVING	Budgeted
Emergency Fund	$_____
College	$_____
Car & Repairs	$_____
Computer	$_____
Other: _____	$_____
SAVING TOTAL:	$_____

FOOD	Budgeted
Restaurants / Eating Out	$_____
School Lunch / Snacks	$_____
FOOD TOTAL:	$_____

CLOTHING	Budgeted
Clothes	$_____
Sports Jerseys / Apparel	$_____
CLOTHING TOTAL:	$_____

TRANSPORTATION	Budgeted
Gas	$_____
Car Insurance	$_____
Oil Changes	$_____
License & Taxes	$_____
TRANSPORTATION TOTAL:	$_____

PERSONAL	Budgeted
Cosmetics / Hair Care	$_____
Music / Technology	$_____
Gifts	$_____
Pocket Money	$_____
Cell Phone	$_____
Other: _____	$_____
PERSONAL TOTAL:	$_____

RECREATION	Budgeted
Movies	$_____
Concerts	$_____
Sporting Events	$_____
Other: _____	$_____
RECREATION TOTAL:	$_____

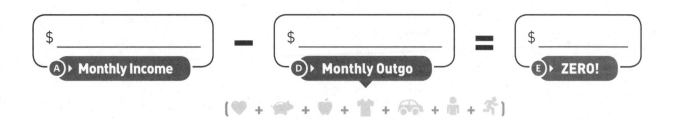

$ _____ Ⓐ ▸ **Monthly Income** — $ _____ Ⓓ ▸ **Monthly Outgo** = $ _____ Ⓔ ▸ **ZERO!**

(♥ + 🐷 + 🍎 + 👕 + 🚗 + 👤 + 🏃)

Chapter Summary

 ## Check for Understanding

Now it's time to check your learning! Go back to the Before You Begin section for this chapter. Place a checkmark next to the learning outcomes you've mastered and complete the "after" column of the Measure Your Progress section.

 ## Build On What You've Learned

Review Real Wealth Building Begins With Your Behavior in Section 1. Fill in the graphic organizer with the seven wealth-building habits. Discuss with your classmates which things you are already doing well and which habits you still need to work on.

1. _____
_____
_____

2. _____
_____
_____

3. _____
_____
_____

7. _____
_____
_____

Wealth-Building Habits

4. _____
_____
_____

6. _____
_____
_____

5. _____
_____
_____

Take Action Challenge

*It's time to practice budgeting using a variety of income levels. Go to **foundationsU.com/budgetnow** for your Take Action Challenge.*

Big Ideas

The following Big Ideas are intended to provide clear focus and purpose to the lessons. Read each statement and think about how what you've learned will affect your current and future decisions. Then, in the space provided, write an "I believe" statement for each of the Big Ideas.

» Do a written budget every month!

_____

» Use the envelope system to help you stay on budget.

_____

» Commit to having good money-management habits.

_____

Money in Review

Matching
Match the following terms to the correct definition below.

A Reconcile   D Budget   G Carbon Check

B Impulse Purchase   E Zero-Based Budget   H Overdraft

C Cash Flow Statement   F Envelope System

1. _____ A written cash flow plan

2. _____ The act of matching your bank statement with your checkbook

3. _____ A cash flow plan that assigns an expense to every dollar of your income, wherein the total income minus the total expenses equals zero

4. _____ An item that is bought without previous planning or consideration of the long-term effects

5. _____ Occurs when money is withdrawn from a bank account and the available balance goes below zero

6. _____ Series of envelopes that are divided into categories (food, entertainment, gas, etc.) and are used to store cash for planned monthly expenses

7. _____ A summary that shows total income and spending for a given time period

8. _____ A copy of each check you write

Illustration
Draw a picture representation of each of the following terms.

Managed Money

Overspending

Multiple Choice

Circle the correct answer.

9. The number-one cause of divorce in North America today is stress and disagreements over money.

    Ⓐ True
    Ⓑ False

10. The envelope system works great for managing spending on things that don't normally have a fixed monthly expense.

    Ⓐ True
    Ⓑ False

11. Which of the following is a consequence of overdrawing your checking account?

    Ⓐ Overdraft fee from your bank
    Ⓑ Bounced check fee from the store
    Ⓒ Stress from money mismanagement
    Ⓓ All of the above

12. Doing a budget does not:

    Ⓐ Make your money go further
    Ⓑ Make overspending more likely
    Ⓒ Show if you are overspending in an area
    Ⓓ Remove guilt and shame sometimes associated with purchases

13. Your monthly budget should include:

    Ⓐ Fixed expenses
    Ⓑ Variable expenses
    Ⓒ Discretionary expenses
    Ⓓ All of the above

Short Answer

Respond in the space provided.

14. What are the reasons cash flow plans sometimes do not work?

    _____

    _____

    _____

15. Why is the zero-based budget the best method of budgeting?

    _____

    _____

    _____

16. Explain why you should always have a cash flow plan.

    _____

    _____

    _____

17. Describe the various payment options that come with a checking account.

    _____

    _____

    _____

18. Why is it important to maintain a file of both paper and electronic financial records?

    _____

    _____

    _____

CHAPTER

What do other high school students know about debt?

We asked students why they think so many people go into debt for things like clothing and other purchases.

....

"Because they don't think about their bills coming up at the time they are using their credit card."

Senior, Nevada

"Because our whole society is so consumed with material things. People base their self-worth on 'stuff.'"

Junior, South Dakota

"We want everything now. We don't want to wait and save up for things."

Sophomore, Kentucky

"People go into debt because credit card companies have made using credit trendy. They even make the credit cards look pretty."

Senior, California

"People don't keep track of their money and are only concerned with the now, not the consequences later."

Senior, Wisconsin

Debt

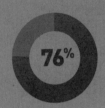

76%

of undergraduate students have a credit card.*

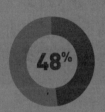

48%

of undergraduate students have four or more credit cards.*

WE'VE ALL BEEN taught that we need to build a good credit score and that debt is a financial tool used to get the things we want. Sadly, as you learned in Chapter 1, borrowing money is so ingrained in our culture that we can't imagine life without it. The truth is, "building a credit score" causes more harm than good. And using debt as a "tool" displays impatience and immaturity in money management. Debt forces us to become slaves financially, and it limits how we spend our money.

*Federal Reserve Survey of Consumer Finances

Before You Begin

 ## Learning Outcomes

Once you've completed this chapter's videos, you will be asked to return to this list of learning outcomes and place a checkmark next to the items you've mastered.

Section 1: Debt: Product, Not Privilege

☐ Identify the costs of using various types of credit.

Section 2: Debunking the Credit Myths

☐ Evaluate and refute the myths associated with debt.

☐ Apply systematic decision making to identify the most cost-effective option for purchasing a car.

☐ Identify various types of mortgage loans and the most cost-effective option for purchasing a home.

☐ Evaluate ways that debt can negatively affect your financial future and how to overcome personal debt.

Section 3: The Credit Score

☐ Describe the elements of a credit score.

☐ Understand how to obtain a credit report.

☐ Explain how a credit score affects creditworthiness and the cost of credit.

☐ Explain the factors that affect a credit score.

☐ Analyze a credit report, indicate the time that certain negative data can be retained, and describe how to dispute inaccurate entries.

Section 4: Credit Bureaus and Identity Theft

☐ Identify organizations that maintain consumer credit records.

☐ Summarize major consumer credit laws.

☐ Develop a plan for protecting personal information.

 ## Key Terms

Get to know the language of money.

» **Annual fee:** A yearly fee that's charged by the credit card company for the convenience of the credit card

» **Annual percentage rate (APR):** Cost of borrowing money on an annual basis; takes into account the interest rate and other related fees on a loan

» **Credit card:** Type of card issued by a bank that allows users to finance a purchase

» **Credit report:** A detailed report of an individual's credit history

» **Credit score:** A measure of an individual's credit risk; calculated from a credit report using a standardized formula

» **Debt snowball:** Preferred method of debt repayment; includes a list of all debts organized from smallest to largest balance; minimum payments are made to all debts except for the smallest, which is attacked with the largest possible payments

» **Depreciation:** A decrease or loss in value

» **Introductory rate:** An interest rate charged to a customer during the early stages of a loan; the rate often goes up after a specified period of time

» **Loan term:** Time frame that a loan agreement is in force, and before or at the end of which the loan should either be repaid or renegotiated for another term

» **Tax deduction:** An expense, such as a charitable contribution, that can be deducted from one's taxable income

✱ **Note:** You may also want to review the following terms from Chapter 1: consumer, credit, debt, interest and loan

Measure Your Progress

Before watching the video, read each statement below and mark whether you agree or disagree in the "Before" column. Then, after watching the video, do it again using the "After" column to see if you changed your mind on any statement.

BEFORE			AFTER	
Agree	Disagree		Agree	Disagree
☐	☐	1. Co-signing a loan is a good way to help a friend or relative.	☐	☐
☐	☐	2. Cash advance and title pawning are needed services but should be used with caution.	☐	☐
☐	☐	3. The typical millionaire drives reliable used cars.	☐	☐
☐	☐	4. Leasing a car is a smart way to drive a newer car for a lower monthly payment.	☐	☐
☐	☐	5. A new car is the largest purchase most consumers make that goes down in value.	☐	☐
☐	☐	6. A home equity loan is a substitute for an emergency fund and a good way to consolidate debt.	☐	☐
☐	☐	7. You need to have a credit card to rent a car or check in to a hotel.	☐	☐
☐	☐	8. It is okay to use a credit card if you pay it off every month.	☐	☐
☐	☐	9. Teens are the number one target of credit card companies today.	☐	☐

JOURNAL QUESTION: INTRODUCTION

What have you heard about "building your credit score"?

_____

_____

_____

CHAPTER

Section 1:
Debt: Product, Not Privilege

2 THE SECOND FOUNDATION
Get Out of Debt

WE LIVE IN A WORLD where it takes a total national economic meltdown to get most people's attention about crazy mortgages and stupid credit card debt! If there's one good thing that's come from the national economic mess of 2008 and beyond, it's that some people are finally getting the message: Debt is dumb!

VIDEO 1.1

Debt Is Everywhere

» Almost _____% of Americans are living paycheck to paycheck. A Reuters survey of 30,600 people found that 68% said it would be somewhat difficult or very difficult if their paychecks were delayed for a week. The problem? Overspending and way too much debt.

» When it comes to debt, if you tell a lie or spread a _____ long enough, eventually it becomes accepted as the _____. The truth is, debt is a product—*the most successfully marketed product in history.*

» The world wants us to believe that debt is a *service* or *reward* that is offered to help consumers. This is simply NOT true!

» Debt has been _____ to us with such intensity for so long that to imagine living without it requires a complete _____ shift—a completely new way of looking at things.

JOURNAL QUESTION: VIDEO 1.1

Explain how debt is actually a product that is bought and sold.

_____

_____

_____

Sadly, it is easier than ever for 18-year-old college students to get credit cards. In response to the 2009 Credit Card Accountability, Responsibility and Disclosure (CARD) Act, the credit card industry has updated its marketing techniques and incentives to now include mailing credit card offers to students and offering promotional and "tangible" gifts to prospective collegiate customers. New policies also allow students to include student loans as a component of the income they cite to qualify for credit cards.

Fox Business

The Devastating Effects of Credit

In 2001, CBS's *60 Minutes II* correspondent Vicki Mabrey reported on the devastating effects credit card marketing had for one college student and his mother. Sean Moyer was an 18-year-old National Merit Scholar with future law school plans when he headed off to the University of Texas in Dallas. Even though he had always worked from the time he was 16, Sean was naïve when it came to credit cards. Like a lot of other freshmen, Sean applied for and received his first credit card when he got to college. Because of credit card debt, Sean was forced to transfer to the University of Oklahoma so he could live at home. By that time, he was working two jobs making minimum wage as a salesperson and gift wrapper for a major department store. One day, his mother knocked on Sean's bedroom door but got no answer. Upon entering, she found him dead; he had hung himself in the closet. Sean Moyer was 22 at the time with more than $14,000 of credit card debt. His mother told *60 Minutes II*, "It just never occurred to me that you could give a credit card to an 18-year-old making minimum wage. When he died, he had 12 credit cards." In 2007, CNN ran a similar story about credit card marketing on campuses and what happened to Sean Moyer. They reported that Sean's mother still receives credit card offers in the mail for her son, despite the fact that he died in 1998.

VIDEO 1.2

A Message From Dave

As a marketer, I have to give the credit card industry some credit. They've done a great job of marketing their product. They've not only gotten nearly every American hooked on their goods, but they've done it in a way that makes the consumer feel special, accepted and as though they've been done a favor. It's kind of scary how good a job they've done, in fact.

Financial Myths Young Adults Fall For

» The first one is the belief that you have to build _____. The credit industry wants you to believe this. Credit is NOT necessary to survive. The truth is there is _____ good reason to go into debt.

» The second myth is that you can spend money on whatever you want while in _____ and pay for it later when you're making more _____.

✴ REMEMBER: Taking on a lot of debt when you're young will limit your options later in life.

» The third myth is that you need a _____ car. You should buy the car you can afford—with cash.

Don't fall for these myths. _____ debt, save for emergencies and large purchases, and learn to say no, even when people around you won't.

JOURNAL QUESTION: VIDEO 1.2

Explain what Dave means when he says, "The borrower is slave to the lender."

_____

_____

_____

Which Credit Card Is Best?

"I'm going to college after I graduate and will need a credit card for various things, such as internet access. Can you recommend one that's better than the others?"

DAVE'S ANSWER: I never recommend using credit cards. NEVER! You can pay for internet access, make online purchases, and buy things in a store with a debit card.

Using a debit card, which is connected to your checking account, means you're spending money that's actually yours. You're not borrowing it from some bank and then paying interest on it. If you don't have money in your account, you won't be making purchases. That's the way it works, and it's the smartest thing you can do.

Credit cards are the quickest way I know to become broke and stay broke for the rest of your life!

Section 2:
Debunking the Credit Myths

A Message From Dave

We weren't born to use debt. Our country was not founded on easy financing and 90-days-same-as-cash. The great fortunes in the history of America weren't built on cash-back bonuses and free airline miles. We've been sold a bill of goods, and it's a total lie. If you tell a lie or spread a myth often enough, loud enough and long enough, eventually the myth becomes accepted as truth. That's where we are with debt in America: trapped in the myth that credit is a normal, healthy part of life.

`VIDEO 2.1`

Money Myths

> **MYTH** If I _____ money to a friend or relative, I will be helping them.
>
> 12

> **TRUTH** The relationship will be strained or _____.
>
> 13

"Our great-grandparents thought debt was a sin. Our grandparents thought debt was dumb. Our parents borrowed on a few things. We borrow on everything."

-DAVE RAMSEY

The average number of credit cards per person is 3.5.

Federal Reserve Survey of Consumer Finances

Money Myths *(Continued)*

MYTH By _____ a loan, I am helping out a friend or relative.

TRUTH The bank requires a co-signer because the person isn't likely to _____. Be ready to pay the loan and have your credit damaged.

MYTH _____ _____, payday lending, rent-to-own, title pawning, and tote-the-note lots are needed _____ for lower income people to help them get ahead.

TRUTH These are horrible, greedy rip-offs that aren't needed and benefit no one but the owners of these companies. They are what's known as *predatory lenders*.

Predatory lenders are modern-day loan sharks who take advantage of people and should be avoided at all costs. So why is the industry still thriving? Because they offer fast cash. But these are serious money traps. Here are reasons you should stay away from this type of lender:

» Payday loans are expensive. If a $100 payday loan costs you $15 for 10 days, that's an annual percentage rate of 400%.

» You can get stuck in a repeat cycle. According to *Center for Responsible Lending Research*, 76% of payday loans are to pay off old payday loans.

SECURED LOANS and UNSECURED LOANS are the two types of loans typically available to borrowers.

An **UNSECURED LOAN** is given to borrowers based on their financial resources or ability to repay the loan. Nothing "secures" the loan. In other words, the lender does not have rights to a specific asset if the loan is not repaid. Personal loans, student loans, and personal lines of credit are examples of unsecured loans.

A **SECURED LOAN** is usually needed when borrowing large amounts of money. The loan is "secured" with collateral. In other words, if you default on the loan and your house was used as collateral, the lender would take the house. Secured loans usually have lower interest rates and longer repayment terms. Automobile loans, mortgages and home equity loans are examples of secured loans.

» Debt grows fast at these rates. It's not unusual to end up owing 4–10 times the amount you originally borrowed.

» Many of these companies have horrible reputations for unethical debt collection practices.

Eighty percent of _____ in America are first-generation rich. That means they started with nothing, did smart stuff, and became millionaires. That's the opposite of what we're talking about here.

MYTH ▶ The _____ and other forms of gambling will make me _____.

TRUTH ▶ The lottery is a _____ on the poor and on people who can't do math.

Texas Tech University did a study on the Texas Lottery and found that, of those who play the lottery, people without a high school diploma spent an average of $_____ a month playing the lottery. College graduates spent $_____ a month on average.

JOURNAL QUESTION: VIDEO 2.1

Explain why co-signing a loan is never a good idea.

_____

_____

_____

Have you ever loaned someone money, only to have it turn into a bad experience?

"My friendship hasn't been the same since I loaned a friend money and didn't get it back. I don't trust him anymore."

Junior, Missouri

"A close friend of mine bought a new car and couldn't afford the payment. I loaned him $300, then he left the state. I couldn't afford to take him to court because of court costs, so I dropped the whole thing."

Junior, Michigan

"I loaned $150 to a friend who never returned it and then claimed that I 'gave' it to him."

Senior, Missouri

"I loaned my mother more than $2,000 to help pay for my 19-year-old brother's car note and college fees. She promised to pay me back but it has been over a year and a half and I haven't received one payment from her. I will never loan money again."

Senior, Georgia

VIDEO 2.2

The Truth About Car Loans

3 | THE THIRD FOUNDATION
Pay Cash for Your Car

The Third Foundation is paying cash for your car. We teach people not to borrow money, period. But there are a few more reasons to avoid financing a new car. For instance, when you purchase a new car, you lose money. If you have a net worth of $1 million, it's not such a big deal. But many people who buy new are broke, living paycheck to paycheck. And that's why they have so much money trouble.

MYTH _____ payments are a way of life, and you'll always have one.
[24]

TRUTH Staying away from car payments by driving reliable used cars is what the typical _____ does. That is how they became millionaires.
[25]

How many times have you heard or said, "I'll *always* have a car payment"? That's the normal way of thinking. But normal is broke. We want to be WEIRD! To get new results, you have to try new things.

So think about this:

» What if you decided to stop messing with car payments?

» What if you invested that car payment every month instead of giving it away to the bank?

» What if we showed you a six-year plan that would put you in free cars for the rest of your life?

» What if that plan also made you a millionaire?

Three huge ways you lose when buying a new car:

1. **Payments.** Spreading the purchase of an automobile over four or five years hinders your ability to pay off debt or save money for that time.

2. **Interest.** Included in the payment, of course, are the interest charges. That means you pay more than the sticker price. It's like buying a $20,000 vehicle for $23,000.

3. **Depreciation.** This is the biggest one. If you purchase a $20,000 car, it will be worth about $8,000 in four years. That's in addition to all the gasoline, maintenance and other stuff. You could buy a $2,000 beater and get the same use out of it for those same four years without taking a $12,000 hit.

Save a few thousand dollars and buy a used vehicle with cash (getting a discount by flashing the money), and you'll ride with a lot more peace of mind.

"If you call my radio show, struggling to get out of debt, you can almost guarantee that the first words out of my mouth will be, 'Sell the car!' If you want to take control of your money, you've got to amputate the out-of-control lifestyle. For most people, that starts with the car payment."

DAVE RAMSEY

JOURNAL QUESTION: VIDEO 2.2

Explain how the "drive free" method of buying a car works.

_____

_____

_____

VIDEO 2.3

The Truth About Car Loans *(Continued)*

MYTH _____ your car is what sophisticated financial people do. You should always lease things that go down in value. There are tax advantages.

TRUTH *Consumer Reports, Smart Money* magazine and a good calculator will tell you that the car _____ is the most _____ way to finance and operate a vehicle.

If you own a business, you can _____ _____ your paid-for car on taxes without making payments for the privilege.

The way to _____ the money lost on things that go down in value is to buy slightly _____.

MYTH You can get a good deal on a _____ car.

TRUTH A new car loses _____% of its value in the first four years. This is the largest purchase most consumers make that goes down in value.

JOURNAL QUESTION: VIDEO 2.3

Explain why leasing a car is a bad idea.

_____

_____

_____

A **CAR LEASE** is a long-term rental agreement; a form of *secured long-term debt.*

"The rich ask, 'How much?' Broke people ask, 'How much down and how much a month?' If you can't pay cash, you can't afford it."

DAVE RAMSEY

The average new-car loan now is at 65 months, a term previously unheard of. Even more distressing is that financing for new cars with terms from 73 months to 84 months—that's six- and seven-year-plus notes—jumped 19.4% in 2012. With these terms, you'll be **upside down** (owe more than the car is worth) almost as soon as you drive off the lot!

The Wall Street Journal

Buying a House

MYTH ▸ I'll take out a 30-year mortgage and pay _____ on it. I promise!
₃₄

TRUTH ▸ Life happens and something else will always seem more important. Never take out more than a _____ -year fixed rate mortgage.
₃₅

The ideal way to buy a house is the 100%-down plan—pay cash for the whole house. Sounds weird, doesn't it? But think how much fun that would be! No mortgage! No payments! If paying cash for a house seems too far out of reach, you can still buy a house if you make wise choices. Save a down payment of at least 10% on a 15-year (or less) fixed rate mortgage, and limit your monthly payment to 25% or less of your monthly take-home pay. You can probably qualify for a much larger loan than what 25% of your take-home pay will give you. But it's not wise to spend more on a house, because then you will be what Dave calls "house poor." Too much of your income will be going out in payments, and that will put strain on the rest of your budget. You won't be able to save and pay cash for things like furniture and cars.

WHAT DO FIXED AND VARIABLE RATES MEAN?

With a fixed rate mortgage, the interest rate is set when you take out the loan, and it will not change. Therefore, your monthly payments will never change. Variable rate mortgages (or adjustable rate mortgages—ARM) will start with a lower rate. This initial rate may stay the same for months or years. But when this "introductory period" is over, your interest rate will change and the amount of your monthly payment will likely go up.

📊 15- or 30-Year Mortgage?

Let's say you're buying a home valued at $250,000 with a $25,000 down payment. That would leave you with a mortgage amount of $225,000. Now let's look at how much you'll pay if you choose a 15- or a 30-year repayment plan.

TOTAL COST OF MORTGAGE

$500,000 »
$400,000 »
$300,000 »
$200,000 »
$100,000 »

30-YEAR PAYBACK:
$485,636
@ $1,349 / Month

15-YEAR PAYBACK:
$341,762
@ $1,899 / Month

$485,636 – $341,762 = **$143,874!**

Choosing the 15-year mortgage saved you **$143,874** and it's done in **half** the time!

30-Year Mortgage   **15-Year Mortgage**

MORTGAGE OPTIONS TO AVOID

ADJUSTABLE RATE MORTGAGES (ARMs): An ARM is a mortgage with an interest rate that changes based on market conditions. The intention is to transfer the risk of higher interest rates to you and, in return, the lender gives a lower rate up front. Since they can qualify for more home, many people find this mortgage appealing; however, as many homeowners learned in the economic downturn, if your rate adjusts higher or you lose your job, your payment can quickly become too much for you to afford.

REVERSE MORTGAGES: A reverse mortgage is when a homeowner borrows against the equity in their home and obtains monthly, tax-free payments from the lender. This mortgage is a bad idea because you are putting a paid-for home at risk, and the fees are horrible. In fact, the FTC claims that reverse mortgages have the most fraud in the mortgage business.

Home Buying Tips

Get your finances in order. The first thing you should do is make sure you are financially ready to buy a house. In other words, you need to be debt-free with a fully funded emergency fund.

Be certain you can afford a new home by asking these questions:

1. Can I make at least a 10% (preferably 20%) down payment?

2. Can I afford a 15-year fixed rate loan?

3. Can I keep the house payments at or below 25% of my monthly take-home pay?

If you answered yes to all three questions, then you can afford a house. You should also be debt-free with a full emergency fund left over after closing. Otherwise, Dave strongly suggests you wait to buy a home.

JOURNAL QUESTION: VIDEO 2.4

Explain why it is better to take out a 15-year mortgage instead of a 30-year mortgage.

_____

_____

_____

Credit Cards

MYTH You need a _____ _____ to rent a car or make a purchase online or by phone.

TRUTH A _____ card does all of that. The only thing you can't do with a debit card that you can do with a credit card is go into debt!

MYTH I pay my _____ _____ off every month with no annual payment or fee. I get brownie points, air miles and a free hat.

TRUTH When you use cash instead of plastic, you spend _____ % less because spending cash hurts.

MYTH I'll make sure my _____ gets a credit card so he or she can learn to be responsible with money.

TRUTH Teens are a huge _____ of credit card companies today. The reason is that the adult market is saturated. Also, researchers have discovered that there is a strong brand loyalty to your first credit card. Therefore, credit card companies are competing to have *their* card be your *first* card.

JOURNAL QUESTION: VIDEO 2.5

Explain the difference between a credit card and a debit card.

_____

_____

_____

"The only man who sticks closer to you in adversity than a friend is a creditor."

UNKNOWN

Researchers studying the neurological impact of big purchases hooked up an MRI to participants and watched their brainwave activity. They found that when people spend cash, it neurologically registers as pain.

Carnegie Mellon Magazine

Credit cards are moving away from a magnetic swipe and moving toward chips in the cards. It's called RFID technology, and all you have to do when you use your credit card is wave it.

"Never spend your money before you have it."

THOMAS JEFFERSON
American founding father

VIDEO 2.6

Debt vs. Wealth-Building

MYTH ▶ Debt is a _____. It should be used to create prosperity.
₄₂

TRUTH ▶ The _____ is slave to the lender.
₄₃

When surveyed, the Forbes 400 were asked, "What is the most important key to building wealth?" _____% replied that becoming and staying _____-free was the number-one key to wealth building.
₄₄ ₄₅

That's because your largest wealth-building tool is your income. When you don't have any *payments*, you have *money*.

⬆ What About Credit Card Rewards?

"My credit card has no annual fee, and I get money back from the credit card company for all of my charges. I only use it for bills and I pay it off every month, so I'm getting money from the credit card company for using their credit card. What's wrong with that?"

DAVE'S ANSWER: I've been doing financial counseling for decades, and I've worked with tens of thousands of people. During that time I've repeatedly met folks who were doing exactly what you are doing, and it has come back to bite them.

When you're talking about credit cards, you're talking about a multibillion-dollar industry designed to do just one thing—separate you from your money. And they're really good at it! They're more than willing to pay you a percentage point back because they know you're going to stumble at some point—and that's when they pounce!

I've talked with hundreds of millionaires, and I've never met one who said they got rich thanks to credit card rebates. They've all just gone about the business of earning money, living on less than they make, and saving. They don't play with snakes because they know, sooner or later, they'll get bitten.

Steps Out of Debt

1. **Quit borrowing more money!**

2. **You must save money.**

3. **Sell something.**

4. **Get a part-time job or work overtime (temporarily).**

5. **Use the debt snowball method.**

   Debt Snowball: List your debts in order from smallest to largest. Pay minimum payments on all your debts except for the smallest one, and attack that one with intensity! Every extra dollar you can get your hands on should be thrown at the smallest debt until it is gone. Then you attack the second one. Every time you pay off a debt, you add its old minimum payment to your next debt payment. So as the snowball rolls over, it picks up more snow. Get it?

   ✱ **REMEMBER:** Even if your other loans have higher interest rates, you should still start with your smallest one first. That way you experience quick wins and build momentum along the way!

JOURNAL QUESTION: VIDEO 2.6

Which credit myths did you believe prior to hearing this lesson? Explain why each of those are myths and not facts.

_____

_____

_____

Borrowing money and failing to pay it back has some serious consequences. Here are some terms commonly used when dealing with debt problems that have gone too far. This is lingo you don't want to experience firsthand.

FORECLOSURE: Process by which the holder of a mortgage sells the property of a homeowner who has not made interest and/or principal payments on time as stipulated in the mortgage contract

REPOSSESSION: Process of a lender taking something back (like a car) for failure to make payments

BANKRUPTCY: A legal procedure for dealing with debt when an individual or business cannot repay what they owe

GARNISHMENT: A court-ordered attachment that allows a lender to take monies owed directly from a borrower's paycheck; only allowed as part of a court judgment

SURRENDER OF COLLATERAL: In a bankruptcy proceeding, a debtor can give up property (collateral) to the creditor in exchange for a clean slate.

DELINQUENCY: Broadly refers to a borrower not being current on his or her payments

The total number of
card holders in the U.S.
is 176.8 million.

Federal Reserve Survey of
Consumer Finances

**WHAT DOES FICO
STAND FOR?**
FICO stands for **Fair Isaac
Corporation**, the company
that created and computes
this credit score. Although
other companies also
compute credit scores,
FICO is the most trusted
and most used score.

Section 3: The Credit Score

VIDEO 3.1

What Your Credit Score Really Measures

MYTH You need to take out a credit card or car loan to "build up your _____ _____."
₄₆

TRUTH The _____ score is an "I love _____" score
₄₇ ₄₈
and is not a measure of winning financially. In fact, it can often mean the opposite. If you were to inherit $10 million tomorrow, it would have NO effect on your credit score!

Some people seem to believe that the credit score is almost as important as oxygen and water. Most of that stems from the fact that we've been beaten over the head with the importance of the credit score since we first learned the difference between a $10 bill and a $5 bill. But it's simply not true. Can you really live without a credit score? Absolutely—and it's actually easier than you'd think. It just takes some foresight, planning and maybe a little patience.

📊 The Five Components of the FICO Score

Don't be fooled into thinking a FICO score measures how well you handle money. Take a look at its five components below.

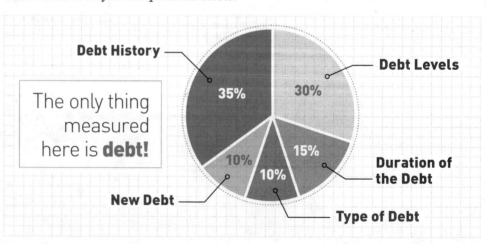

The only thing measured here is **debt!**

Debt History 35%
Debt Levels 30%
Duration of the Debt 15%
Type of Debt 10%
New Debt 10%

No Credit Score? No Problem!

1. **How do I rent an apartment?** Most apartments will work with you if you can provide first and last month's rent as well as a security deposit. Get a rental history referral from your previous landlord. If it's your first time renting, you might have to look around for a little while. But you'll be able to find someone to work with you.

2. **How do I take out a mortgage?** If you don't have a credit score, you should focus on one thing—making sure you have a large down payment. If you've never gone into debt, that shouldn't be too difficult, right? Without a credit score, the down payment, as well as your job and how long you've been employed in that line of work, are big factors. You'll also want an outstanding history of rental and utility payments. Look for a mortgage company that uses a process called manual underwriting, sometimes called "non-traditional credit" or "no credit score" lending.

3. **What if an employer wants to see my credit score during the interview process?** This is a growing trend, but it mainly affects people in the financial industry— banks, mortgage brokers, investment companies and so on. Again, the key here is to learn their process up front and explain why you don't have a credit score if they ask you about it.

The average college undergrad is carrying about $2,169 in credit card debt. Graduate students carry an average of $8,162 in credit card debt.

Investopedia.com

There are a lot of companies that measure credit, but two major credit scoring systems are FICO and VantageScore (which the three credit bureaus jointly created). FICO ranges from 300 to 850, and VantageScore ranges from 501 to 990. Remember, a credit score measures the risk of your not repaying debt; it is not a measure of financial success.

CREDIT BUREAUS are also commonly referred to as consumer reporting agencies or credit reporting agencies.

JOURNAL QUESTION: VIDEO 3.1

What does a credit score measure?

_____

_____

_____

Section 4:
Credit Bureaus and Identity Theft

In a recent survey, one in four teens didn't know the difference between a debit card and a credit card.

MSN Money

VARIOUS FORMS OF CREDIT REPAYMENT

Note: We recommend that you NEVER borrow money. Period.

Installment: This is credit that you use to borrow money and promise to repay in equal amounts over a specific period of time.

Revolving Credit: This is credit in which a pre-established amount of money is borrowed repeatedly as long as the account is in good standing.

Layaway: An agreement in which the seller reserves an item for a buyer until the buyer pays for the item in full

What Is a Credit Bureau?

» A **credit bureau** is an agency that researches and collects individual credit information and sells it for a fee to creditors so they can make a decision on granting loans. Typical clients include banks, mortgage lenders, credit card companies and other financing companies.

» Individual account information is removed from your credit report seven years after the last activity on the account, except for Chapter 7 bankruptcy, which stays on for 10 years.

» Beware of credit clean-up scams. The only information that may be legally removed from a credit report is inaccurate information.

» The three main credit bureaus are: **Experian**, **TransUnion** and **Equifax**.

Correcting Credit Report Inaccuracies

A recent study by the Federal Trade Commission questions the reliability of the credit reporting industry. It is believed that as many as 40 million Americans have a mistake on their credit report. Twenty million have significant mistakes.

✱ **REMEMBER:** You should check your credit report annually. You can do this for free at foundationsU.com/report.

Identity Theft

Identity theft is the fastest growing _____-_____
crime in North America today. ₄₉

Warning signs that you may have had your identity stolen:

» Checks disappear from your checkbook.

» You receive a bill from a credit account you didn't open.

» Your credit report shows accounts you didn't open.

» Unauthorized charges appear on your cell phone or bank accounts.

» A collection agency calls about a debt you didn't incur.

» You are turned down for a loan, mortgage or other form of credit because of unauthorized debts on your credit report.

» Bank and billing statements don't arrive on time.

What you should do if you think you are a victim:

» Obtain a copy of your credit report and look for any suspicious activity.

» Place a _____-_____ alert on your credit bureau report (stays on for 90 days without a police report). ₅₀

» If your purse or wallet is stolen, cancel all cards immediately and get replacements. Also put a "stop payment" on all lost or stolen cards.

» File a _____ report and keep a copy of the report for your personal records. ₅₁

» Report any suspicious charges and accounts to the appropriate credit issuers and credit bureaus immediately via the phone and in writing. Cancel the accounts.

The 2013 Identity Fraud Report released by Javelin Strategy and Research states that in 2012 identity fraud incidents increased by more than 1 million victims. Fraudsters stole more than $21 billion, the highest amount since 2009.

Identity Theft *(Continued)*

» Remember, this is _____. You owe _____ and should pay nothing.

» Contact the fraud-victim division of the three main credit reporting companies and furnish _____.

» Be persistent. This will take some time. You now have a new _____.

Obviously, you're never too young to be careful with your personal information. Here are some tips to protect yourself from identity theft:

» Use a paper shredder and destroy credit card offers and other documents with your personal information.

» Check your credit report annually. Many people don't even know that their identity has been stolen. Bottom line, you can't fix the problem if you're not aware of it.

» Never print your Social Security number or driver's license number on your checks.

» Sign the back of your debit card and write "PHOTO ID REQUIRED."

» Create strong passwords using a combination of letters, characters and numbers.

» Keep passwords and personal information confidential.

» Purchase identity theft protection.

Consumer Credit Laws

The U.S. Congress enacted the Fair Credit Reporting Act (FCRA) in 1970. The FCRA was intended to address concerns over consumer credit report accuracy, privacy and fairness.

» **Accuracy:** Prior to the FCRA, consumers were unable to challenge errors in their credit reports. The FCRA gives consumers the right to review the contents of their credit report file and dispute inaccurate information.

HOME EQUITY LOAN

A home equity loan means borrowing money against your house. Like any other debt, home equity loans are a bad idea. They often come with higher, variable interest rates and if there comes a time when you can't make the payments, you risk losing your home!

CREDIT COUNSELING

Companies that offer consumer credit counseling services can help you get better interest rates and lower payments, but at a price. When you use one of these companies and then try to get a home mortgage loan, you will be treated the same as if you had filed Chapter 13 bankruptcy.

Real debt help is found only in changing your behavior.

In short, debt management companies are out. Hard work is in. Change your financial behavior and change your life—for good. True debt management is about one thing: you controlling your money.

» **Privacy:** To protect consumers' privacy, the FCRA requires that a person or organization have a "permissible purpose" (or legitimate need) for checking a person's credit information.

» **Fairness:** The FCRA grants consumers the right to know if a decision to deny them credit or other adverse action against them was based on information in a credit report file. Creditors must notify consumers if they deny credit based on a credit report file, and they must also tell the consumer which of the three credit bureaus provided the report. The act also allows consumers to receive one free credit report per year.

✱ NOTE: There are several other credit laws of which you should be aware. Please refer to the glossary under "credit laws" for more information.

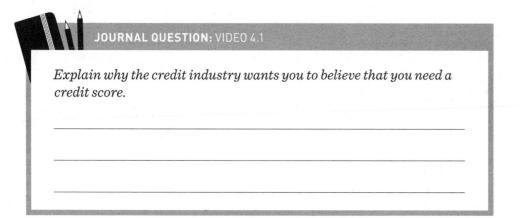

JOURNAL QUESTION: VIDEO 4.1

Explain why the credit industry wants you to believe that you need a credit score.

_____

_____

_____

Chapter Summary

Check for Understanding

Now it's time to check your learning! Go back to the Before You Begin section for this chapter. Place a checkmark next to the learning outcomes you've mastered and complete the "after" column of the Measure Your Progress section.

Big Ideas

The following Big Ideas are intended to provide clear focus and purpose to the lessons. Read each statement and think about how what you've learned will affect your current and future decisions. Then, in the space provided, write an "I believe" statement for each of the Big Ideas.

» The Second Foundation: Get Out of Debt

_____

» The Third Foundation: Pay Cash for Your Car

_____

» The FICO score is an "I love debt" score!

_____

Take Action Challenge

*We've told you that it is important to check your credit report every year, even if you don't use credit. So why not do it now? It's easy and it's free. You can get a free copy from each of the three credit agencies—TransUnion, Experian and Equifax—once a year. Go to **foundationsU.com/report** to get started.*

✱ NOTE: The vast majority of teens ages 14–18 do not have a credit file. Ideally, you will receive a simple rejection message from AnnualCreditReport.com. However, if there is a credit file and it is full of errors, you'll need to work on clearing them up. Contact all three credit bureaus and consider putting a freeze on your credit.

 # Build On What You've Learned

*You've learned that there are many myths in our culture when it comes to the use of credit. Review the chapter and select **five credit myths that were most surprising** to you. Fill in both the myth and truth for each of them in the graphic organizer below.*

CREDIT MYTHS	CREDIT TRUTHS
1. _____ _____	1. _____ _____
2. _____ _____	2. _____ _____
3. _____ _____	3. _____ _____
4. _____ _____	4. _____ _____
5. _____ _____	5. _____ _____

Money in Review

Matching

Match the following terms to the correct definition below.

> **A** Credit Report   **D** Credit Score   **G** Credit Card
>
> **B** Loan Term   **E** Debt Snowball   **H** Annual Fee
>
> **C** Depreciation   **F** Annual Percentage Rate

1. _____ Cost of borrowing money on an annual basis; takes into account the interest rate and other related fees on a loan

2. _____ A decrease or loss in value

3. _____ A detailed report of an individual's credit history

4. _____ Time frame that a loan agreement is in force, and before or at the end of which the loan should either be repaid or renegotiated for another term

5. _____ Type of card issued by a bank that allows users to finance a purchase

6. _____ A measure of an individual's credit risk; calculated from a credit report using a standardized formula

7. _____ A yearly fee that's charged by the credit card company for the convenience of the credit card

8. _____ Preferred method of debt repayment; includes a list of all debts organized from smallest to largest balance; minimum payments are made to all debts except for the smallest, which is attacked with the largest possible payments

Illustration

Draw a picture representation of each of the following terms.

Debt

Debt Free

Multiple Choice

Circle the correct answer.

9. You must establish credit in order to buy a house.

    Ⓐ True
    Ⓑ False

10. If you are a victim of identity theft, you are only responsible for paying back half of the debt.

    Ⓐ True
    Ⓑ False

11. Which of the following is *not* a factor in determining a FICO score?

    Ⓐ Paying cash for all purchases
    Ⓑ Getting a personal loan from a bank
    Ⓒ Using credit cards
    Ⓓ Taking out a mortgage on a house

12. Which of the following is *not* a good idea for getting out of debt?

    Ⓐ Quit borrowing money
    Ⓑ Get a part-time job or work overtime
    Ⓒ Borrow money from your parents to pay off the debt
    Ⓓ Sell something

13. Which of the following things cannot be done with a debit card but can be done with a credit card?

    Ⓐ Rent a car
    Ⓑ Purchase something online
    Ⓒ Go into debt
    Ⓓ Purchase an airline ticket

Short Answer

Respond in the space provided.

14. Why is an adjustable rate mortgage (ARM) a bad idea?

    _____
    _____
    _____

15. Explain why financing a car is a bad idea.

    _____
    _____
    _____

16. Describe the negative consequences of taking on debt. What effect can debt have on your future?

    _____
    _____
    _____

17. What are some things you can do to protect your personal information?

    _____
    _____
    _____

18. Explain how the debt snowball works.

    _____
    _____
    _____

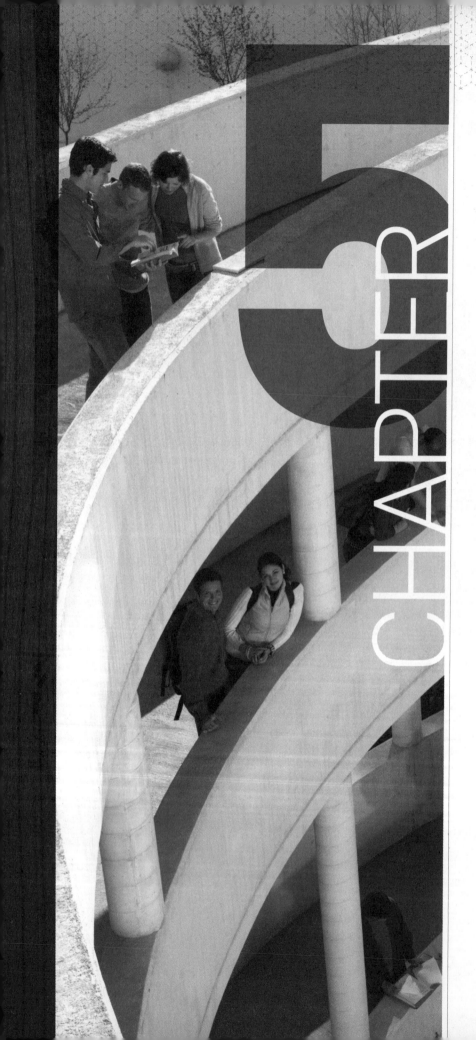

CHAPTER 5

How are other students planning for life after high school?

We asked students what education and career plans they have after graduation.

....

"I plan on going to business school and starting my own company."

Senior, Washington

"I plan to go to college for four or more years and find a job that pays well. I don't know what yet, to be honest."

Junior, Michigan

"I want to go to college and become a dental assistant or a school teacher."

Junior, Utah

"I am going to culinary arts school."

Sophomore, Arizona

Life After High School

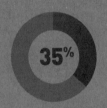

35%

of college-bound students have never discussed college funding with their parents.*

80%

of college-bound students have not projected the total amount of money they will need to graduate college.*

ONCE YOU GRADUATE from high school, a world filled with endless opportunities is set before you. While it's exciting, it can also be difficult to navigate. Aside from choosing a career, you'll need to select an education path that will help you achieve your individual career goals. These choices will greatly affect your financial well-being after college. As a young adult, you will have a marketing target on your back. Credit cards and student loans might seem like an enticing solution when money is tight, but you must be prepared to avoid these financial hazards by having a plan.

*Education Insider

Before You Begin

 ## Learning Outcomes

Once you've completed this chapter's videos, you will be asked to return to this list of learning outcomes and place a checkmark next to the items you've mastered.

Section 1: Beware and Be Wise

☐ Understand the long-term impact of student loans.

Section 2: Start With the End in Mind

☐ Identify reasons for not taking on debt to fund your education.

Section 3: Cash-Flow Your College Education

☐ Develop a plan to attend college without acquiring debt.

☐ Demonstrate how to apply for financial aid.

Section 4: Education Options for the 21st Century

☐ Identify the educational requirements, training and cost for your career of choice.

☐ Analyze post-high school education and career training options.

 ## Key Terms

Get to know the language of money.

» **Free Application for Federal Student Aid (FAFSA):** A form that is completed annually by current and prospective college students to determine their eligibility for financial aid

» **Grant:** A form of federal or state financial aid that does not need to be repaid; usually given to students who demonstrate financial need

» **Scholarship:** A form of financial aid that does not need to be repaid; usually awarded on the basis of academic, athletic or other achievements

» **Work study:** A program that allows students to work part time while continuing their studies

Measure Your Progress

Before watching the video, read each statement below and mark whether you agree or disagree in the "Before" column. Then, after watching the video, do it again using the "After" column to see if you changed your mind on any statement.

BEFORE			AFTER	
Agree	Disagree		Agree	Disagree
☐	☐	1. I have a good idea as to what college I want to attend after graduation, and cost was a major factor in that decision.	☐	☐
☐	☐	2. I believe that it is possible to go to college debt free.	☐	☐
☐	☐	3. Everyone uses student loans to attend college. I don't see any reason I should be different.	☐	☐
☐	☐	4. I have considered technical school and other 21st-century educational options for my career of choice.	☐	☐
☐	☐	5. I have discussed with my parents how we plan to cover the expense of my college education.	☐	☐

JOURNAL QUESTION: INTRODUCTION

Not every career requires a four-year degree. Have you researched the education requirements for your career of choice? If so, what education options do you have? If not, research the education requirements for your career choice(s) and write them below.

_____

_____

_____

There is roughly $1 trillion in total outstanding student loan debt in the United States today.

Consumer Finance Protection Bureau

Nearly 20 million Americans attend college each year. Of that 20 million, close to 12 million—or 60%—borrow annually to help cover costs.

The Chronicle of Higher Education

CHAPTER 5

Section 1: Beware and Be Wise

VIDEO 1.1

Considering all your career and education options after high school can be overwhelming. After all, some of your decisions may open doors to endless opportunities while others may have long-term consequences. The good news is, planning ahead for your career and education will help you find those opportunities. And learning about the dangers of student loans and credit cards will allow you to avoid those long-term consequences of a few bad decisions. Bottom line, you've got to beware and be wise.

Wise People Invest in Themselves

Before anything else and throughout your whole life, the best investment you can make is in yourself! Here are some ways you can invest in yourself.

» Charlie "Tremendous" Jones said, "Five years from now you will be exactly the same person you are today except for the _____ you read and the _____ you meet."

» First, you have got to _____. Leaders are readers!

» Reality TV and video games are great _____, but they're just entertainment.

"This debt has ruined relationships."

"My name is Andrea, and I currently have $112,623 in debt. The short version of my story is simply that I used student loans for my entire education, which is how I earned a bachelor's degree in Early Childhood Education. I'm currently a preschool teacher's assistant, and I only make $24,000 a year. As a result, I have a second job and work about 80 hours a week, every single week. The majority of 'my' student loan debt is a 'stupid tax,' because I co-signed on a student loan for an ex-boyfriend. I constantly tell my friends to work hard and save to pay cash for everything they buy. A few of them have listened, but I pray that no one else has to endure what I'm going through. This debt has ruined relationships, and there are many days that I can't quite picture the end."

✱ **DISCUSS:** If Andrea could do college over again, what things might she choose to do differently? Why?

» The average _____ reads one nonfiction book a month!
₅

» Your net _____ as an adult will be the average of the five people you hang out with the most.
₆

» The people you put in your life influence your career, your _____ and how you spend your money.
₇

» Have some _____ who have already had some success.
₈

The average student loan debt has now surpassed $27,000 for an undergraduate degree.

The Project on Student Debt

JOURNAL QUESTION: VIDEO 1.1

What is your plan for after high school graduation?

_____

_____

_____

VIDEO 1.2

Beware of the Student Loan Myth

Not all careers require the same type of post-secondary education. We are going to show you how to come up with the most cost-effective education plan for your career of choice. If a four-year college is the best education option for you, we want to show you how to do it without student loans. Believing that student loans are a "good debt" because they are a path to getting an education is a *myth*. You can get your education without becoming a slave to debt.

4 THE FOURTH FOUNDATION
Pay Cash for College

» Our culture thinks student loan debt is okay—it seems totally _____. Some people even call it "good debt."

» When you receive your financial aid award package for college, you'll see a list of all different types of awards like _____ and grants.

  ✱ **BE AWARE:** Student loans will be listed in your financial aid award package as well.

» A student _____ is NOT an award! It will take years to pay it back, plus you'll have to pay interest.

» _____ is owing anything to anyone for _____ reason.

» There is no such thing as a "good debt."

» The total estimated student loan debt in our country is one _____ dollars.

» Millions of people can't afford to make their student loan _____ every month.

Debt Free

It might be tough to turn down what society considers "good debt" and find other ways to pay for college. But is it worth the extra work? Yes! If you make the sacrifice and effort right now, you'll keep yourself from digging a hole you'll have to start climbing out of the moment you receive your college degree. How will you do it? By the end of this chapter, you'll have more options than you can even imagine to get a great college education completely debt free.

A Message From Dave

Piling up student loans throughout your college career is like keeping a monster locked in your closet. Every semester, that beast gets bigger and meaner and nastier. Then six months after you graduate, whether you have a job or not, that monster busts out and starts wrecking your life! All of a sudden you have to make every decision based on tackling that mountain of debt you neglected for four years. It controls where you live, what you do, and what kind of job you can take. That's definitely not a good way to start your career!

That's why we want to teach you how to get through college debt free. You'll learn about career education and training options, grants, scholarships, work programs, and how to "shop" for a college that's within your budget.

I know college is a lot of hard work, and I know it can be a lot of fun. I want you to have plenty of both. But I don't want you to end up with a four-year degree with 40 years of payments on it! Do whatever it takes to stay out of debt—whether it's student loans or credit cards. Then when you graduate, you'll really have a world of options because you won't be worried about the time bomb of student loan payments waiting for you six months later!

Studies show that 30% of student loan borrowers drop out of school, and then have to find a way to pay back their student loans on a high school graduate's salary.

Washington Post

JOURNAL QUESTION: VIDEO 1.2

Why might people refer to student loans as "good debt"?

_____

_____

_____

Two-thirds of college students graduate with student loans.

CNN Money

Debt is normal. **Be weird!**

Section 2:
Start With the End in Mind

VIDEO 2.1: THERE ARE NO FILL-INS IN THIS SECTION.

So you've decided that you will continue your education at a four-year college. How do you plan to pay for it? If student loans are part of your plan, you may want to rethink that. Listen to the stories in this chapter and decide how you really want to begin your post-college life.

You can start making decisions right now that will allow you to avoid the mounds of debt that so many young adults begin their life with. One of those choices is to cash-flow (pay as you go) your college education.

Many people believe it's impossible to go to college without taking out a loan. They'll say things like, "The economy is down," or "Tuition is so expensive," or "I have no other options." Everyone takes out loans, so it's not a big deal, right? We hear it all the time. It's easy to think that because it's what we see all around us in our culture. In fact, almost 70% of college students graduate with debt! But just because it's easy to sign those student loan notes doesn't mean it's the only way. And it definitely doesn't mean it's the best way.

 "I regret going to college *when* and *how* I did."

"I regret going to college when and how I did. I didn't know how a credit card worked when I started college at 17. I was told I would get a fantastic job and wouldn't have to worry about those loans. I graduated a year ago, have the same jobs I had during college, and am deferring most of my $40,000 of loans because I can't pay the bills. I am desperate to be a stay-at-home mom, and I can't because of my loans. I worked the entire time I went to college, but all of my money went toward my living expenses and a car, so I was not able to put any toward tuition."

Don't Steal From Your Future

Take a look at some of these statistics:

» The total estimated student loan debt outstanding is more than $1 trillion.

» Of the total outstanding student loan debt, approximately $85 billion is past due.

» The percentage of student loan borrowers who paid on time without postponing payments or becoming delinquent? A mere 37%. In other words, 63% of borrowers had a hard time paying back their loans.

» Nearly 30% of student loan borrowers wind up dropping out of school, and more than 50% of borrowers at two-year for-profit colleges never finish.

Think about it: You don't want to steal all of your future possibilities from yourself by going into debt to get your degree.

"It's not hard to decide what you want your life to be about. What's hard is figuring out what you're willing to give up in order to do the things you really care about."

Bittersweet: Thoughts on Change, Grace, and Learning the Hard Way

About 41% of borrowers fall behind on their student loan payments in the first five years.

nytimes.com

JOURNAL QUESTION: VIDEO 2.1

Imagine if your reality at age 24 was that you were $70,000 in debt but your income was only $30,000. Write down some words describing how you might feel.

_____

_____

_____

Section 3:
Cash-Flow Your College Education

VIDEO 3.1

What does it mean to cash-flow your college education? To "cash-flow" simply means to pay with cash as you go, instead of using credit or debt.

Plan Ahead

» You need a _____! Start now. Get help from your parents and school counselor along the way.

» Planning for college involves more than just ACT scores and college applications. You must understand how much it is going to cost (that includes tuition, books and living expenses) and know how you are going to pay for it.

Get Good Grades

» One thing you can do _____ _____ is get good grades.

» Good grades do more than just get you into the school and career you want. They also help you get free money! Yes, scholarships go to those who earn them.

» Making good grades and scoring well on the ACT or SAT will set you apart from the crowd.

» How would you like to get paid to be a high school student? Well, the fact is your hard work now can turn into money later. Think about it.

Shop Around

» It's a good idea to _____ your choices down to
six schools or less. During this process, consider each
school's degree programs, living expenses and tuition.

» Keep in mind that _____ _____ doesn't
always mean _____ _____. Your future
happiness, success and income will have very little to
do with the prestige or name recognition of the college
you attend.

» Attending a community college for your first two years is
a great way to knock out your freshman and sophomore
years at a low cost. If you plan to continue your education
after your two-year degree, work closely with your
advisor to make sure the classes you take are going to
_____ to your four-year university of choice.

» Consider attending a state school instead of a private or
out-of-state school, which will have much higher tuition.
You must "shop" for the best price for your education in
the same way you comparison shop on any large
purchase. Don't be sold on prestige!

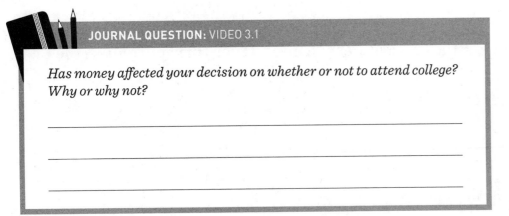

JOURNAL QUESTION: VIDEO 3.1

Has money affected your decision on whether or not to attend college?
Why or why not?

_____

_____

_____

CASE STUDIES

Kayla O. "I'm going to
finish college with an RN
degree and zero debt by
attending a community
college. I pay $4,000 a year,
while other people I know
are going to the university
up the road and spending
$20,000 a year for the
same education. In the
end, we have to take the
same national test to be
an RN, so why not keep the
$16,000?"

Applying for Financial Aid

In order to make the most of _____ college, you've got to focus on the specifics like filling out your financial paperwork, researching scholarships, and finding part-time work opportunities.

Fill Out the FAFSA Form

» The _____ (Free Application for Federal Student Aid) is the first step to receiving any kind of financial aid. Whether you are interested in scholarships, grants, loans or other financial aids, you'll need to submit this form.

» The FAFSA form needs to be completed each year you are in college. The sooner you turn in the form (by January or February), the more likely you are to get financial help because some federal _____ is awarded on a first-come, _____-served basis.

» Remember, student loans are bad news. Make sure you ask that the student loans be _____ from your funding.

» You'll need your family's tax information as you complete the FAFSA. Keep in mind, if you turn it in online, the process moves faster.

Explore Grants

» _____ are golden.
27

» Federal and state governments offer grants that are usually need-based. The FAFSA will determine which grants you qualify for. Examples include the Federal _____ _____ and state-specific grants.
28

» Grants are free _____!
29

Research Scholarships

» Another form of free money is _____.
30

» You should never pay to apply for scholarships. And do not give out your Social Security number when you apply.

Where to Find Scholarships

While merit-based scholarships are the most popular, there are countless other types available. If you have a unique talent or skill set, there is a good chance of finding an award that's just right for you. With a little research, you'll be amazed at both the variety and availability of these scholarships. Here are some types of scholarships:

» University scholarships for academics, athletics, clubs, etc.

» Community scholarships like the Boys and Girls Club or Rotary Club

» Local business scholarships exist to promote their organization

» Private donors might include relatives or other individuals

» Student-specific scholarships exist for almost every characteristic you can think of

» Unique scholarships for a variety of hobbies, talents and interests

Talk to your guidance counselor and search online to see what award opportunities are out there for you. Don't be put off by a small award. Every dollar adds up, and there is no limit to the number of scholarships for which you can apply.

Applying for Financial Aid *(Continued)*

When to Visit the Financial Aid Office

» If you get stuck at any point in the process, just stop by your college's _____ _____ office.
₃₁

» If your financial situation has changed, a parent has been laid off, or a medical situation has come up, it's important to visit the financial aid office. Your financial aid can be re-evaluated and possibly increased.

» Talk to a financial aid officer as soon as an emergency arises. They will offer you advice, encouragement or help.

Research Work Opportunities

Get a part-time job.

» Research shows that students who work up to _____ hours a week have the highest grade point averages of any type of student in college because they often develop good time-management skills.

» Research also shows that working *more than* 20 hours a week may affect your grades negatively.

Work on or off campus.

» You can find jobs _____ _____ that offer flexible schedules for students in a variety of roles. These jobs usually pay more than work study.

» On-campus jobs may pay you directly or pay toward your tuition bill.

Eight out of every 10 students who drop out of college say financial trouble was the main reason.

Attrition Study at Idaho State University

CASE STUDY

William M. worked full time on the second shift for a company that offered tuition reimbursement. "Burning the candle at both ends was the hardest thing I've ever done, but it was worth it when I finished summa cum laude," he said.

"If you live like no one else, later you can live like no one else!"

DAVE RAMSEY

» Usually the school provides hourly positions that pay minimum wage; the good news is you can often study as you work. Check with the financial aid office to see what jobs are offered.

Make Sure You Have an Emergency Fund

» The First Foundation is to establish an emergency fund of $500. Since you are taking this course in high school, you should already have your emergency fund in place by the time you graduate.

✱ REMEMBER: In spite of what society teaches us, credit cards are NOT emergency funds!

» As you work in the summer and save money for your school bill, set aside a separate amount in an emergency fund. If something bad happens during school, you will have some funds to fix the problem so you don't have to drop out of school.

THINGS TO CONSIDER
The smartest investment you can make is in yourself. As a young adult, you should have two goals: continue your education and stay out of debt.

More than 78% of freshmen plan to work during their college years.

National Freshman Attitudes Report

Average Student Loan Balance: 2005–2012

Student loan debt is the only form of consumer debt that has grown since the peak of consumer debt in 2008. Balances of student loans have exceeded both auto loans and credit cards, making student loan debt the largest form of consumer debt outside of mortgages.

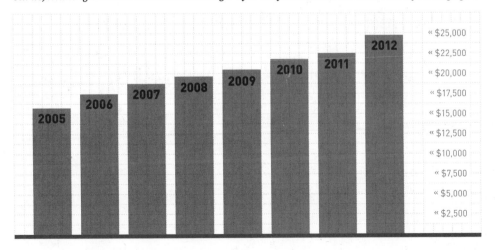

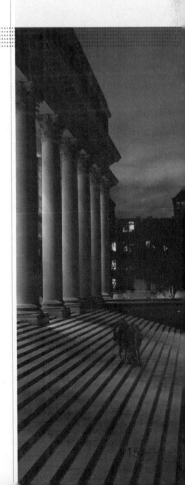

Live on a Zero–Based Budget

Now is a good time to review the basics of budgeting.

» Make sure you do a monthly budget. Having a zero-based budget is a great way to manage your money and live on less than you make.

» In order to live on less than you make, you've got to decide ahead of time how much you'll spend, save and give each month. Then, stick to it!

1. **Spending.** Break it down into categories, like food, gas, etc.—and make sure you keep your spending in check.

2. **Saving.** It's never too early to start saving, whether it's for a new car, next semester's tuition or a video game.

3. **Giving.** Make it a priority to help other people. Give to your church or an organization that shares your beliefs.

Avoid Student Loans

» Remember, you have two goals:

1. Stay in school.

2. Stay out of debt.

» Avoid student loans! The average repayment period for a student loan is 10 years if you make the minimum payment each month. You will pay more interest if you go beyond 10 years.

Consider Attending a School Close to Home

» Attending a community college or state university that allows you to live at home is a great option for reducing the cost of living expenses, even if it is only for your first two years of school.

» Collegedata.com reported that the average cost of room and board in 2012–2013 ranged from $9,205 at four-year public schools to $10,462 at private schools.

Your Determination Will Pay Off

So there it is. When it comes to college (and life in general), debt is not the answer. You have countless options when it comes to getting a great college education completely debt free! It might mean working hard and planning ahead. But when you're out of college and you actually get to keep your paycheck instead of sending it all to student loan debt, you will be so glad you did.

The choices you make in the next few years will affect the next 40 years of your life. You'll have much more freedom to pursue your dreams and do exactly what you want to do. Now that's a great way to begin your future!

THINGS TO CONSIDER

Living off campus can cost a lot of money! You'll probably be excited to be out on your own when you begin college. But think about the savings if you just put that off for a year or two. You might be wise to reconsider that dorm or apartment.

JOURNAL QUESTION: VIDEO 3.2

What money-saving options will you consider in order to cash-flow your college education?

_____

_____

_____

Section 4:
Education Options for the 21st Century

VIDEO 4.1

Be a Lifelong Learner

Many students and their parents believe that a four-year college degree is necessary to compete in the job market. College is not for everyone, and it is possible to build a career without investing in an expensive college education. Twenty-first-century education comes in many forms. Remember, however, that even if a traditional four-year college isn't for you, it is still important to invest in yourself. Learning is a necessary lifelong venture regardless of your career choice or specific educational needs. If you do your research, you can be sure you're deciding on a career path that reflects your passions as well as your financial goals. It's important to assess what your interests are, how you like to learn, and what motivates you. For example, do you like to build things, sit behind a computer, or interact with people? Once you've decided on a career, here are some college alternatives to consider.

Trade School

Trade schools allow students to learn basic _____ _____ in two years or less because technical schools typically cut out many of the general courses required by traditional universities. Also, since trade schools are often directly tied into the employment needs of their region or state, prospective employers often seek new hires from trade school graduates.

Certifications

Students who are looking to learn specific skills can look into free or low-cost _____ found online, at community colleges, or through government-funded programs.

Self-Education

Start reading books, blogs and trade magazines in your field of choice. Attend conferences and local events. Meet people and find a mentor. You may also want to attend online courses specific to your field.

On-the-Job Training

_____-_____-_____ training is just that. You, the employee, train at the place of work while you are doing the actual job. Usually a professional trainer serves as the course instructor and uses a combination of hands-on activities and formal classroom training.

Associate's Degree

An associate's _____ is a two-year degree that can offer a variety of benefits including lower cost than four-year colleges, specialized training and a flexible schedule that allows you to work while you earn your degree. Whether it is your first step toward earning a bachelor's degree or the beginning of your career, an associate's degree may be a great option. Career fields such as fashion design, nursing, cardiovascular technology and criminal justice are offered at the associate's level.

Budget Builder

Cash-flowing your post-high school education will take some planning. Go to foundationsU.com/5 to build it into your budget!

"I have never let my schooling interfere with my education."

MARK TWAIN
American author

Starting a Business

Maybe you'd like to _____ your own business. While there is always risk involved, if you have passion and an entrepreneurial spirit, it might be right for you. Be sure to create a solid business plan and establish financial resources first. Stick with a debt-free plan. Remember to be enthusiastic about your venture. Many people who don't necessarily make "good" traditional students make the best entrepreneurs because of their passion and people skills. Be prepared to work hard and know that there will be some bumps in the road.

Military

The military isn't for everyone, but it has helped a lot of people get through college debt free while giving them the honor of serving their country.

Remember, post-secondary education is not a one-size-fits-all plan. With so many options, you have the opportunity to create your own educational experience that allows you to follow your passions and meet your goals.

A Message From Rachel

We've talked a ton about going to college, but some of you might feel like college isn't for you—and that's okay. There are alternatives to getting a four-year degree, many of which result in great career options. Before making a firm decision to pass up college, though, I'd like to encourage you to do two things: ask yourself why, and make sure you have a solid plan for your future.

Ask yourself why you don't feel like college is right for you—and be honest when you answer. Don't lie to yourself, okay? It may help to talk through your reasons with a parent or adult that you trust. You might find that you're just like the rest of us—a little scared of the unknown. You know, "What will the first day be like?" or "What if I can't make the grades?" Those worries are normal—and most of them will be old news by the second week of school.

But maybe you'll discover college really isn't for you. That's when you need a plan. Just like other areas of life, most successful careers aren't stumbled upon. They're built with a plan. And no, a solid plan doesn't include living in your parents' basement until you meet a lovely lady who will take over cooking and cleaning duties from your mom. It just doesn't work that way, guys!

Everyone is different—and thank goodness, right? It's totally okay if your life after high school doesn't look the same as your friends'. What's not okay is settling because of uncertainties. If you're willing to put in the work, then you've got what it takes to conquer your fears and reach your dreams. Don't let anything hold you back from reaching your potential and pursuing a career that you love!

CASE STUDIES

Anthony K. began working toward a U.S. military academy appointment when he was a freshman in high school. He attended the U.S. Naval Academy, receiving a $250,000 education for free.

Kate J.'s husband attended college paid for by the Air Force while they scrimped to pay for books. He worked part time and was even deployed to Iraq, but he graduated in five years with a 4.0 grade point average. He now has his dream job—USAF pilot.

JOURNAL QUESTION: VIDEO 4.1

Think about what careers you might be interested in pursuing. What type of education or training will you need to enter that field?

_____

_____

_____

Chapter Summary

 ## Check for Understanding

Now it's time to check your learning! Go back to the Before You Begin section for this chapter. Place a checkmark next to the learning outcomes you've mastered, and complete the "after" column of the Measure Your Progress section.

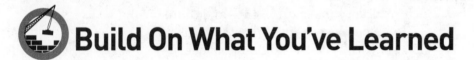 ## Build On What You've Learned

Review: Securing Financial Aid

Write what you know about each of the following components of a financial aid package.

Grants: _____

Scholarships: _____

Work Study: _____

Loans: _____

 ## Big Ideas

The following Big Ideas are intended to provide clear focus and purpose to the lessons. Read each statement and think about how what you've learned will affect your current and future decisions. Then, in the space provided, write an "I believe" statement for each of the Big Ideas.

» The Fourth Foundation: Pay Cash for College

_____

» Not all careers require four-year degrees.

_____

» Begin planning now!

_____

 # Take Action Challenge

If you don't know the educational requirements for your specific career choice, take this opportunity to research the information. Fill in this graphic organizer with the information you gather. If you are undecided among several career options, be sure to research the educational requirements and the cost of each career program.

AFTER HIGH SCHOOL

I want to be a: _____

Other options
I'm considering: _____ _____

I'll prepare for this position
with one of the following educational options:

OPTION 1

NEXT STEPS:

- ☐ Community college
- ☐ 4-year college
- ☐ Trade school
- ☐ Certification
- ☐ Self-education
- ☐ On-the-job training
- ☐ Start a business
- ☐ Military

COST:	TIME:
$ _____	_____

OPTION 2

NEXT STEPS:

- ☐ Community college
- ☐ 4-year college
- ☐ Trade school
- ☐ Certification
- ☐ Self-education
- ☐ On-the-job training
- ☐ Start a business
- ☐ Military

COST:	TIME:
$ _____	_____

OPTION 3

NEXT STEPS:

- ☐ Community college
- ☐ 4-year college
- ☐ Trade school
- ☐ Certification
- ☐ Self-education
- ☐ On-the-job training
- ☐ Start a business
- ☐ Military

COST:	TIME:
$ _____	_____

START YOUR **CAREER** DEBT FREE!

Money in Review

Matching

Match the following terms to the correct definition below.

(A) FAFSA	(D) "Good Debt"	(G) Mentorship
(B) Work Study	(E) Scholarships	(H) Trade School
(C) Grant	(F) Associate's Degree	

1. _____ A developmental partnership through which one person shares knowledge, skills and perspective to foster the personal and professional growth of someone else

2. _____ A form of federal or state financial aid that does not need to be repaid

3. _____ A program that allows students to work part time while continuing their studies

4. _____ An undergraduate academic degree awarded by colleges upon completion of a course of study lasting two years

5. _____ A form that is completed annually by current and prospective college students to determine their eligibility for financial aid

6. _____ A money myth that portrays student loans as the only financial option when it comes to funding one's college education

7. _____ A merit-based form of financial aid that does not need to be repaid; usually offered on the basis of academic, athletic or other achievements

8. _____ A type of higher learning school that focuses on job skill training for specific career fields rather than academics in liberal arts

Illustration

Draw a picture representation of each of the following terms.

Student Loans	Financial Peace

Multiple Choice

Circle the correct answer.

9. Our culture thinks student loan debt is normal and that it's an acceptable way to pay for college.

    (A) True

    (B) False

10. A four-year degree is necessary regardless of what career you're pursuing.

    (A) True

    (B) False

11. The total estimated student loan debt outstanding (unpaid) in the U.S.

    (A) $1 billion

    (B) $1 trillion

    (C) $10,000

    (D) $7 trillion

12. Which of the following is *not* a good option when it comes to paying for your education?

    (A) Get a part-time job

    (B) Plan ahead

    (C) Ask your parents to take out a loan

    (D) Fill out the FAFSA

13. Which of the following are ways that you can invest in yourself?

    (A) Find a mentor

    (B) Read books

    (C) Surround yourself with people who have similar goals and ambitions as you

    (D) All of the above

Short Answer

Respond in the space provided.

14. Explain how you can get an education debt free after high school.

    _____

    _____

    _____

15. Based on what you've learned, do you believe it is realistic to graduate debt free? Why or why not?

    _____

    _____

    _____

16. Write down three reasons why you should avoid student loans.

    _____

    _____

    _____

17. Select one of the student stories in this chapter (section 1 or 2) and describe the effect student loan debt had on that person's life.

    _____

    _____

    _____

18. What excites you the most about life after high school?

    _____

    _____

    _____

CHAPTER 6

What do other high school students know about consumer awareness?

We asked other high school students to share their favorite television commercials.

....

"I like the Super Bowl commercials. They show how much competition there is between companies."

Senior, Utah

"I like the mayhem commercials the best."

Junior, Missouri

"My favorite is the 'Is it better to be faster or slower' commercial."

Junior, Tennessee

"I like the commercials with the baby talking about online investing."

Senior, North Carolina

"I like the one where they ask the little kids questions and they come up with funny answers."

Sophomore, Alabama

Consumer Awareness

26%

of teens have placed
an order online
in the past three
months.*

40%

of teens say they are
currently saving.*

MARKETING IS POWERFUL! Think about it—almost every single purchase you've made started with advertising. But be careful. As you learned in Chapter 4, debt is also marketed to you. Some salespeople don't want you to think about the product's total cost; they want you to think in terms of how much down and how much a month. Buyer beware!

*Marketingvox, Rand Youth Poll, Seventeen, Packaged Facts

Before You Begin

Learning Outcomes

Once you've completed this chapter's videos, you will be asked to return to this list of learning outcomes and place a checkmark next to the items you've mastered.

Section 1: Buyer Beware

☐ Identify ways companies compete for your money.

☐ Be familiar with marketing strategies that encourage people to go into debt or finance large purchases.

☐ Evaluate how peer pressure can affect spending decisions.

☐ Summarize factors that influence consumer decisions.

Section 2: Buyer's Remorse

☐ List five steps you should take before making a major purchase.

Section 3: Opportunity Cost

☐ Evaluate the role opportunity cost plays in purchasing decisions.

☐ Describe the effect of inflation on buying power.

Key Terms

Get to know the language of money.

» **Branding:** The promotion of a product or service by identifying it with distinct characteristics (usually associated with public perception, quality or effectiveness)

» **Brand recognition/awareness:** Refers to the public's ability to recall and recognize a brand by its logo, jingles, packaging, etc.

» **Buyer's remorse:** Feeling regret or concern after making a large purchase

» **Caveat emptor:** Latin term for "buyer beware"

» **Financing:** To buy an item with credit; paying over time

» **Marketing:** The process of communicating the value of a product or service to customers

» **Opportunity cost:** Refers to the financial opportunity that is given up because you choose to do something else with your money

» **Significant purchase:** An amount of money you spend, usually $300, that causes some pain to part with

Measure Your Progress

Before watching the video, read each statement and select what you believe to be the correct answer. Then, after watching the video, return to this activity and correct your answers if necessary.

BEFORE & AFTER

1. What percentage of "90-days-same-as-cash" purchases are not paid in 90 days and convert to payments?

   ☐ 25%   ☐ 50%   ☐ 75%   ☐ more than 75%

2. The average cost of a 30-second television advertisement during the 2013 Super Bowl was:

   ☐ $1 million   ☐ $2 million   ☐ $3 million   ☐ $4 million

3. The average American was exposed to almost 560 advertisements daily in 1971. Today that number is closer to:

   ☐ 1,500   ☐ 2,500   ☐ 3,000   ☐ more than 5,000

4. A Harvard University study found that for every hour of television you watch each week, your yearly spending increases by an average of:

   ☐ $50   ☐ $100   ☐ $200   ☐ $500

5. The fashion category accounts for about _____ percent of teen spending.

   ☐ 10   ☐ 25   ☐ 40   ☐ 75

JOURNAL QUESTION: INTRODUCTION

How does advertising affect your buying decisions?

_____

_____

_____

WHY ARE WE SO MARKETED TO?

The U.S. is the most capitalistic country in the world. Capitalism is an economic system based on a free market, profit motive, open competition and private ownership of the means of production. This market is driven by the economic law of supply and demand. Companies promote consumer demand by marketing their products.

TEEN SPENDING HABITS AT A GLANCE

- 55–60% of teens say their parents contribute more than half of their spending dollars.

- The fashion category accounts for roughly 40% of teen budgets.

- Approximately 79% of females and 76% of males shop online, and respondents indicated that roughly 18% of their spending is online.

2013 Taking Stock With Teens Survey, Piper Jaffray Companies

Section 1: Buyer Beware

VIDEO 1.1

The Most Marketed-to Culture in History

WE LIVE IN THE MOST marketed-to culture in the history of the world! If you are going to have financial peace, you are going to have to develop a resistance to that marketing. It's not that buying things is bad. But buying too many things, with money you don't have, to impress people you don't really like—that's a bad idea.

» "Caveat emptor" means _____ _____.

» We're not saying that you can't have a good time with your money. Remember, we want you to _____ like no one else so later you can live like no one else.

» We want to sacrifice to win and then we want to _____ the winning. There's nothing wrong with buying a good product.

» A good salesman has a servant's heart, knows how to sell, and is professional—all of which can make the whole process pretty _____.
  4

» Companies use every angle to aggressively compete for our _____.
  5

» Companies that are not sophisticated and aggressive in their marketing or do not have a marketing budget generally do not stay open.

» Competition is _____ for the consumer dollar.
  6

JOURNAL QUESTION: VIDEO 1.1

Why is it important for consumers to be aware of marketing tactics?

_____

_____

_____

"He who buys what he does not need steals from himself."

UNKNOWN

The Super Bowl is known almost more for its commercials than for the football game. The average cost of a 30-second television spot during the 2013 Super Bowl was $4 million. These ads were viewed in roughly 53.3 million households.

USA Today

What's Wrong With Financing a Purchase?

"What's wrong with buying things on 12-months-same-as-cash?"

DAVE'S ANSWER: It's a stupid idea. First off, if I buy the item with cash, I'll get a better deal. Plus, if you play with snakes, you'll get bitten. If they record your payment wrong and it's late, they'll backcharge you through the entire term of the deal at about 24–38% interest. You'll spend the next year and a half cleaning up this mess. It actually happened with one of our clients here. If you can't save up and pay for the item with cash, you can't afford to buy it!

VIDEO 1.2

Four Common Marketing Tactics

When you turn on the TV, listen to the radio, surf the web, or walk into the mall, you are stepping into battle—a battle for your dollars. Today, companies use every angle imaginable to aggressively compete for your money. The purpose of advertising is to inform, tease and persuade consumers to purchase products.

When you're aware of these techniques, you are more _____ as consumers. Here are four common marketing strategies:

1. One of the techniques is _____ selling. People who know how to sell spend thousands of dollars and hours sitting in a classroom learning how to talk to you—to serve you, to _____ you in your decision to buy their stuff.

2. The second technique is _____. They use money and easy payments as a marketing tool. They don't want you to think about how much something actually costs, rather how much down and how much per month.

I Want to Buy Something, But Can I Afford it?

How do you know when you can afford something? When you have the cash to pay for it! Here are two common financing plans you should avoid:

90-Days-Same-As-Cash

If you pay within 90 days, there are no finance fees. But if you pay late, you will be charged interest for the entire 90 days. What if you have good intentions of paying it off before the 90 days is up? On average, about 80% of customers do not pay it off in 90 days. Life happens. The best intentions are often interrupted by life.

Zero Percent Interest

Look out for the 0% interest trap on car loans! The truth is that 0% financing is nothing more than a really good marketing tool. It has worked so well for the auto industry that other types of retailers, particularly in furniture and electronics, have adopted this method of marketing. In reality, less than one third of all consumers qualify for 0% financing. For the other two thirds, well, they've got you where they want you: in the store and wanting to buy. For those that do qualify for 0%, sellers often make up for the lost finance charges by increasing the price of the product.

THE ECONOMIC LAW OF SUPPLY AND DEMAND

The theory that, in a free market economy, prices are determined by the interaction of supply and demand; an increase in supply will lower prices if not accompanied by increased demand, and an increase in demand will raise prices unless accompanied by increased supply.

For every hour of television per week you watch, you spend an average of $200 extra a year.

Harvard University

What are some of your favorite brands (soft drink, clothing, etc.)? Why do you like them?

_____

_____

_____

VIDEO 1.3

Four Common Marketing Tactics *(Continued)*

3. Other media like TV, radio and internet use

    _____ to sell products. How does repetition
    11
    work? In advertising, repetition means repeated
    exposure. Over time, repeated messages become familiar
    and accepted as true. Companies behind the ads are
    willing to pay for such repetition because it works!

4. When it comes to marketing they also use product

    _____.
    12

    ## Types of Product Positioning

    » **Brand Recognition:** When marketing causes you to
       position a product in your mind to be associated with
       a certain _____.
       13

JOURNAL QUESTION: VIDEO 1.3

Describe one way advertising has played a role in something you've purchased.

_____

_____

_____

Have you ever wanted to know what was really important to someone? Look at their checkbook entries. Are they spending a lot on "stuff" like entertainment, clothes, friends, etc.? People spend their money on things most meaningful to their heart. "For where your treasure is"—the money you spend or save—"there your heart will be also" (Matthew 6:21).

25% of Christmas shoppers will still be paying off the bills come next Christmas! The average consumer takes at least six months to pay off holiday bills.

The Wall Street Journal

If a $1,200 purchase is charged on a credit card at 17% interest and only the minimum payments are made, it will take almost 20 years to pay it off and will cost an additional $2,076 in interest, bringing the total cost of that $1,200 purchase to $3,276!

The Wall Street Journal

VIDEO 1.4

Types of Product Positioning *(Continued)*

» **Color:** Color _____ when you're doing product positioning. Color has an impact on consumer reaction to a product. [14]

» **Shelf Positioning:** Companies pay for prime shelf position in stores. It's a _____ shelf position. It is meant to influence *impulse buying*. [15]

» **Packaging:** The _____, the look and the feel of the package are all meant to have an impact on you. [16]

There's no reason to be paranoid. But marketers are very sophisticated—so we should at least _____. [17]

JOURNAL QUESTION: VIDEO 1.4

Have you ever bought something you thought would make you happy, but in the end it didn't?

_____

_____

_____

Section 2: Buyer's Remorse

VIDEO 2.1

Significant Purchases

Your body goes through physiological changes when you make a significant purchase. You sweat. Your eyes dilate. Your pulse rate changes. Proteins and endorphins are released.

» A "significant purchase" is normally anything over $_____.
   ₁₈

» Buyer's _____ is when you wake up the next day and regret your purchase.
   ₁₉

» We all have that spoiled, grocery store kid living inside of us. His name is _____.
   ₂₀

» When it comes to spending, adults devise a _____ and
   ₂₁
   _____ it.
   ₂₂

» When it comes to big purchases, the right way to do it is to _____ _____ and pay cash.
   ₂₃

JOURNAL QUESTION: VIDEO 2.1

Can you think of anything in your home that was bought but never or rarely used?

_____

_____

_____

The average U.S. household has 52 unused items around the house worth a total of $3,100.

eBay/Nielsen Survey

Describe a money goal that you currently have.

"Saving up enough to buy a nice used car."

Sophomore, Kansas

"Saving $20 per week."

Junior, Washington

"I'm trying to save up $800 for a new set of tires."

Senior, Massachusetts

"My current money goal is to pay off my car and save more money for college."

Junior, Pennsylvania

Budget Builder

Thinking about making a significant purchase? You'll need to save up for that! Go to foundationsU.com/6 to add a sinking fund to your budget.

"Many a man thinks he is buying pleasure, when he is really selling himself to it."

BENJAMIN FRANKLIN
Author, inventor and political theorist

OPPORTUNITY COST
The true cost of something in terms of what you have to give up to get the item; the benefits you would have received by taking the other action.

Section 3: Opportunity Cost

VIDEO 3.1

Develop Power Over Purchase

Because it's always easy to spend more than you make, you must develop _____ over _____. It doesn't matter how much money you make. If you have a spending plan and power over purchase, you can win with money. Having power over purchase involves following these steps:

1. Wait _____ before making a purchase. Take the time to consider whether it is a need or a want. And make sure you've budgeted for it!

2. Consider your buying _____. No amount of stuff equals _____ or fulfillment. People sometimes get _____ and _____ confused. You buy fun, but you can't buy happiness. Happiness is where you are right now. Claim it for yourself!

3. Never buy anything you do not _____. Particularly financial products like insurance or investments.

4. Consider the "_____ cost" of your money—which means that money spent *here* cannot be spent *there*. Whenever you make a choice, you must pass up other opportunities. Take your time and make the right decision.

5. Seek wise _____. Young adults who are not yet married should find an accountability partner—someone with whom you can discuss big purchases. Once you are married, you should seek the counsel of your spouse.

If you follow these steps, you will limit your spending and make purchases that you're proud of—and you will have financial peace.

* NOTE: You'll learn more about investing and retirement planning in Chapter 8.

JOURNAL QUESTION: VIDEO 3.1

Explain why it is important to develop power over purchase.

_____

_____

_____

How Does Inflation Affect Your Buying Power?

INFLATION can be described as the persistent increase in the cost of goods and services or the persistent decline in the buying power of money.

Regardless of how you describe it, inflation basically means your dollars buy less than they used to. You must consider inflation when planning for future expenses, especially retirement. So what should you do?

1. Pay attention to the long-term rate of inflation. This can make inflation trends more predictable.

2. Be sure to consider inflation in your investment planning.

3. Factor a realistic inflation expectation into your financial planning. For instance, what might you expect your cost of living to be by the time you retire?

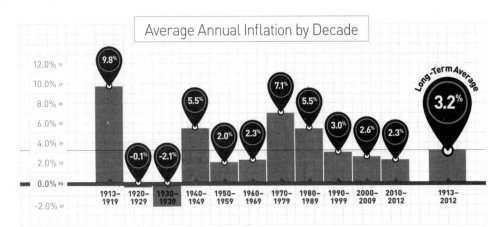

Average Annual Inflation by Decade

Decade	Inflation
1913–1919	9.8%
1920–1929	-0.1%
1930–1939	-2.1%
1940–1949	5.5%
1950–1959	2.0%
1960–1969	2.3%
1970–1979	7.1%
1980–1989	5.5%
1990–1999	3.0%
2000–2009	2.6%
2010–2012	2.3%
1913–2012 (Long-Term Average)	3.2%

Chapter Summary

Check for Understanding

Now it's time to check your learning! Go back to the Before You Begin section for this chapter and place a checkmark next to the learning outcomes you've mastered. Review the Measure Your Progress section and correct your answers if necessary.

Build On What You've Learned

Describe three instances where peer pressure has influenced your decision about a purchase.

3 Times Peer Pressure Influenced Your Purchasing Decision

1

ITEM/EVENT:
_____
_____

PEER PRESSURE:
_____
_____
_____
_____
_____

2

ITEM/EVENT:
_____
_____

PEER PRESSURE:
_____
_____
_____
_____
_____

3

ITEM/EVENT:
_____
_____

PEER PRESSURE:
_____
_____
_____
_____
_____

Take Action Challenge

Imagine that you inherited $5,000. Come up with three things that you could do with the money. Then describe the opportunity cost of each choice.

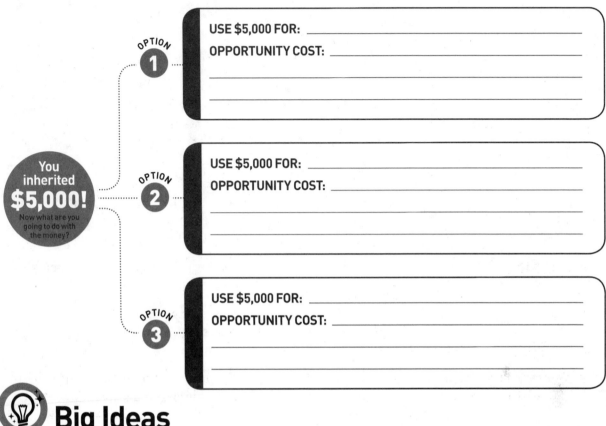

OPTION 1

USE $5,000 FOR: _____

OPPORTUNITY COST: _____

_____

_____

You inherited **$5,000!** Now what are you going to do with the money?

OPTION 2

USE $5,000 FOR: _____

OPPORTUNITY COST: _____

_____

_____

OPTION 3

USE $5,000 FOR: _____

OPPORTUNITY COST: _____

_____

_____

Big Ideas

The following Big Ideas are intended to provide clear focus and purpose to the lessons. Read each statement and think about how what you've learned will affect your current and future decisions. Then, in the space provided, write an "I believe" statement for each of the Big Ideas.

» Don't buy things with money you don't have.

_____

» Develop *power over purchase.*

_____

» Consider the *opportunity cost* of your purchases.

_____

Money in Review

Matching

Match the following terms to the correct definition below.

A Opportunity Cost   **D** Buyer's Remorse   **G** Marketing

B Significant Purchase   **E** Financing   **H** Brand Recognition

C Branding   **F** Caveat Emptor

---

1. _____ To buy an item with credit; paying over time

2. _____ The promotion of a product or service by identifying it with distinct characteristics (usually associated with public perception, quality or effectiveness)

3. _____ Latin term for "buyer beware"

4. _____ An amount of money you spend, usually $300, that causes some pain to part with

5. _____ Refers to the financial opportunity that is given up because you choose to do something else with your money

6. _____ Feeling regret or concern after making a large purchase

7. _____ Refers to the public's ability to recall and recognize a brand by its logo, jingles, packaging, etc.

8. _____ The process of communicating the value of a product or service to customers

Illustration

Draw a picture representation of each of the following terms.

Inflation

Power Over Purchase

Multiple Choice

Circle the correct answer.

9. As a consumer, you should consider inflation in your investment and retirement planning.
    - **A** True
    - **B** False

10. If you don't have cash on hand, financing a significant purchase is a good option.
    - **A** True
    - **B** False

11. Which of the following is not a need?
    - **A** Food
    - **B** Housing
    - **C** Eating out
    - **D** Utilities

12. The purpose of advertising is to:
    - **A** Inform the consumer
    - **B** Tease the consumer
    - **C** Persuade the consumer
    - **D** All of the above

13. Which of the following is not a common marketing strategy?
    - **A** Providing financing options
    - **B** Making the customer do product research
    - **C** Personal selling
    - **D** Repetition

Short Answer

Respond in the space provided.

14. Explain why financing a purchase is a bad idea.

15. Why should you always consider the opportunity cost when making a significant purchase?

16. What are the five steps you should take before making a significant purchase?

17. What effect does inflation have on purchasing power?

18. Summarize factors that influence consumer decisions.

905

CHAPTER 7

What do other high school students know about bargain shopping?

We asked other high school students to describe how they have saved money on a purchase.

....

"I negotiated the price of my vehicle by pulling cash out of my pocket. I got it for $350 less than the asking price."

Senior, Oklahoma

"I cut coupons with my dad when I was little. When we went shopping, he would give me the money he saved by using the coupons."

Junior, Maine

"I find and purchase products online for cheaper than they are in the store. This saves me both time and money."

Senior, Oregon

"I bought a $500 dress for $45 at a consignment shop—and I looked like a million dollars at prom that spring!"

Senior, California

"I waited a couple of months for the price to go down on something I wanted and then bought it."

Junior, Georgia

Bargain Shopping

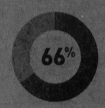

66%

of teens say they
know how to shop
for the best deal
when making
a purchase.*

77%

of teens consider
themselves super
savers as opposed
to big spenders.*

EVEN IF YOU'RE not a spender by nature, finding a great bargain on something you really want will send a rush down your spine. It's just plain fun to find a deal! However, if you want to find the absolute best bargains, you will need to do three things: learn how to negotiate, have patience, and know where to find great deals. Now let the fun and games begin!

*Charles Schwab Teens & Money Survey (2011)

Before You Begin

 ## Learning Outcomes

Once you've completed this chapter's videos, you will be asked to return to this list of learning outcomes and place a checkmark next to the items you've mastered.

Section 1: Bargain Shopping: Part of a Healthy Financial Plan

☐ Understand how shopping for bargains is part of a healthy financial plan.

☐ Analyze and use the three keys to getting bargains: Learn how to negotiate, have patience, and know where to find great deals.

Section 2: The Seven Basic Rules of Negotiating

☐ Develop skills for negotiating deals on products or services.

☐ Understand that integrity and honesty are important when it comes to negotiating with others.

Section 3: Places to Find Great Deals

☐ Know the best places to shop for deals.

☐ Evaluate the benefits of not buying brand-name products, taking advantage of seasonal shopping, buying slightly outdated products, etc.

 ## Key Terms

Get to know the language of money.

» **Auction:** A public sale in which property or items of merchandise are sold to the highest bidder

» **Consignment shop:** Retail store where people sell items and the owner of the shop gets a percentage of the sale

» **Cost-benefit analysis:** The process of quantifying costs and benefits of a decision

» **Estate sale:** Type of yard sale with more items, usually the entire contents of a household

» **Foreclosure:** Process by which the holder of a mortgage sells the property of a homeowner who has not made interest and/or principal payments on time as stipulated in the mortgage contract

» **Integrity:** Having to do with a person's honesty and moral attributes

» **Markup:** The difference between the wholesale price and retail price

» **Negotiate:** To bargain for a lower price

» **Walk-away power:** The ability to walk away from a purchase when negotiating

Measure Your Progress

Before watching the video, read each statement below and mark whether you agree or disagree in the "Before" column. Then, after watching the video, do it again using the "After" column to see if you changed your mind on any statement.

| BEFORE | | | AFTER | |
Agree	Disagree		Agree	Disagree
☐	☐	1. Most of the items at a pawn shop are stolen.	☐	☐
☐	☐	2. Learning to be quiet is actually a powerful tool in negotiation.	☐	☐
☐	☐	3. A seller who senses that you are attached to an item will be less likely to negotiate a deal.	☐	☐
☐	☐	4. In certain circumstances, it is okay to stretch the truth to get a bargain.	☐	☐
☐	☐	5. Most countries, except for the U.S., use negotiating as a way of life.	☐	☐

JOURNAL QUESTION: INTRODUCTION

Explain the best deal you've ever negotiated.

_____

_____

_____

16–18% of Americans will shop at a thrift store during a given year; about 12–15% will shop at consignment/resale shops.

America's Research Group

"The bargain that yields mutual satisfaction is the only one that is apt to be repeated."

B.C. FORBES
Scottish financial journalist and author

BARGAINING is a type of negotiation in which the buyer and seller of a good or service dispute the price that will be paid and the exact nature of the transaction. Bargaining is an alternative pricing strategy to fixed prices.

Section 1: Bargain Shopping: Part of a Healthy Financial Plan

VIDEO 1.1

It's Okay to Want a Better Deal

THIS IS GOING TO BE A FUN LESSON! It's about how to buy stuff and get the best possible bargain. When you get a good deal the right way, everyone wins. You get what you want, and the seller gets your money, which is what he wants. You both feel good about it.

Does negotiating with someone sound strange? Americans are horrible at it. You need to think globally. Practically everywhere outside the U.S., negotiation is a way of life. If you've ever traveled outside the U.S., you've seen it.

Bottom line: It's okay to want a better deal. In fact, saving money should be a part of your healthy financial plan. It's not immoral to want to save more of your hard-earned money. You're not hurting the other party as long as you follow some basic principles of negotiating.

It's proper to get a great deal if you:

1. Have in no way _____ the truth.

2. Have not set out to _____ the other party.

3. Have created a _____-_____ deal.

The First Key to Getting Huge Bargains

» The first key to opening the door to huge bargains is learning to _____ everything. Everything is negotiable! Make getting a bargain a way of life.

» Win-win deals really work, so don't be _____ to ask for the deal. If you gather information from the people you are dealing with, you both can get 100% of what you want. Then there is no harm done to either party, making it a win-win scenario.

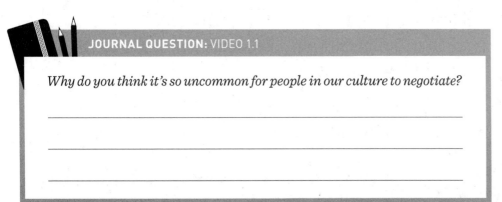

JOURNAL QUESTION: VIDEO 1.1

Why do you think it's so uncommon for people in our culture to negotiate?

_____

_____

_____

People in other cultures routinely use negotiation when buying and selling goods.

"Let us never negotiate out of fear. But let us never fear to negotiate."

JOHN F. KENNEDY
35th president of the United States

The Benefits of Being a Wise Consumer

Being a wise consumer involves developing a variety of skills—from product research to careful comparative analysis. The benefits are not just cost-related. Wise consumers also enjoy improved health and the knowledge that they have made a positive impact on the larger social and even global environment. Using a cost-benefit analysis approach to your buying decisions will make you a wise consumer.

HOME ECONOMICS: Making the right choices as a consumer will usually yield savings. Follow the bargain shopping tips in this chapter for great savings.

HEALTH: Making informed decisions about what foods to buy will promote your physical health.

SOCIETY: Your choices as a consumer have an impact on the larger social and even global environment and economy. Decisions like whether to buy a product manufactured overseas or pay more to support your local business community are things to consider.

"The love of truth is the stimulus to all noble conversation. This is the root of all the charities. The tree which springs from it may have a thousand branches, but they will all bear a golden and generous fruit."

ORVILLE DEWEY
American minister

Section 2:
The Seven Basic Rules of Negotiating

VIDEO 2.1

Negotiate With Integrity

Getting a great deal doesn't happen by accident, nor does it always happen just because you bothered to ask. Remember, this is a negotiation, and that means it's a conversation with give and take. Here are what we call "The Lucky Seven" rules that can help you make the most of every single negotiation:

1. When negotiating, *always* tell the absolute _____.[6]
    Not telling something you know to be true is also lying.

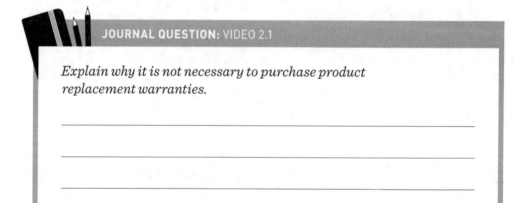

JOURNAL QUESTION: VIDEO 2.1

Explain why it is not necessary to purchase product replacement warranties.

_____

_____

_____

Know How to Score a Good Deal

2. Use the power of _____. The use of cash is becoming less and less common. But if you walk into a store fanning yourself with a handful of bills, you'll get some attention—and increase your power of negotiation. Here's why:

   • Cash is _____.

   • Cash is _____.

   • Cash has _____.

3. Understand and use "_____-_____ power." If you are not prepared to walk away from the purchase, you will lose your ability to negotiate. Don't get emotionally attached to the item.

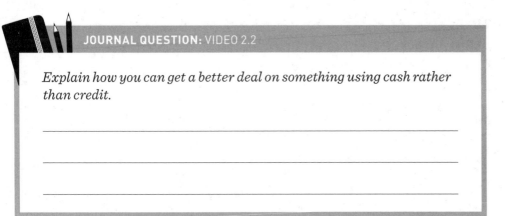

JOURNAL QUESTION: VIDEO 2.2

Explain how you can get a better deal on something using cash rather than credit.

_____

_____

_____

Do you have any experience negotiating overseas?

"I bartered in Mexico and paid $3 for a ring that started at $10."

Senior, Florida

"It's so fun to negotiate in Germany and see how low you can get the seller to go on his price."

Junior, New Mexico

"I got a $50 chain for $15."

Junior, Michigan

"Once I negotiated and paid half the price listed."

Senior, Missouri

"You can bargain at the straw market in the Bahamas. I talked the sales rep at a purse shop down from $150 to $40."

Senior, Georgia

HOW DOES THE GOOD GUY, BAD GUY TECHNIQUE WORK?

One salesperson pretends to be your friend, helping you get the best deal. But every time you get close to making the deal, the salesperson (the "good guy") says he has to get his manager's approval for that price. He goes away and comes back claiming his manager (the "bad guy") won't approve the deal. Dave recommends bypassing the good guy, bad guy technique by requesting to speak directly to someone who has the authority to negotiate the deal.

VIDEO 2.3

Know How to Score a Good Deal *(Continued)*

4. _____ _____. Don't talk too much. If you're trying to buy something, it's not your job to come up with a good price. Make the seller work for your business.

5. "That's not _____ _____." When the person trying to make the sale gives the price, just look him in the eye and say those words. Then be silent. At that point, it's up to him to change the deal.

6. The _____ guy, _____ guy technique is a negotiating tool that you should be aware of. When negotiating with a salesperson, don't fall for this. Neutralize the situation by going around the salesperson. Communicate directly with the supervisor who has the authority to negotiate the deal.

JOURNAL QUESTION: VIDEO 2.3

Explain why silence is powerful when negotiating a deal.

_____

_____

_____

Seal the Deal

7. Use the "If I" _____-_____ technique. You use this one near the end of the deal, after you've pretty much figured out the lowest price possible. The point is to agree to a price, but then throw something else into the deal. For example, "Okay, if I take the car for that price, you've got to throw in new wipers and floor mats."

"The Lucky Seven" rules can get you incredible deals on the stuff you buy every day, but they only work if you actually use them. Have some fun with them and enjoy the process! If you are patient, willing to negotiate, and educated about what items are on sale during certain seasons, you'll be saving big before you know it.

The Second Key to Getting Huge Bargains

The second key to opening the door to huge bargains is having _____. Our collective, consumer lack of patience always makes headlines whenever a hot new tech gadget comes out, doesn't it? Those who buy the moment something new hits the market will always pay the highest price. Save some money—be patient!

Don't get _____ to a purchase. Being emotionally attached to a purchase will always cost you more money. Think about those $50 concert T-shirts!

THE MOST COMMON TYPES OF CONSUMER FRAUD

According to a survey issued by the Federal Trade Commission, the most common types of consumer fraud reported were for bogus weight-loss products, nonexistent foreign lotteries, unauthorized buyer club enrollments, dishonest prize promotions and fraudulent work-at-home programs. The FTC study also found the following results:

- 25- to 34-year-olds issued the most complaints.

- Those without high school diplomas were more likely to be fraud victims.

- Those who reported having more debt than they could handle were more likely to be victims of frauds involving credit repair and debt consolidation.

There are currently more than 25,000 resale, consignment and Not For Profit resale shops in the United States.

The Association of Resale Professionals

The Third Key to Getting Huge Bargains

The third key to opening the door to huge bargains is knowing _____ to _____ deals. Finding great buys is like a treasure hunt. The more you sniff out bargains, the better you'll be at it.

* REMEMBER: Really good deals aren't necessarily found underneath a giant banner that reads "SALE!" Don't fall for a "lower" price that's still not a *good* price.

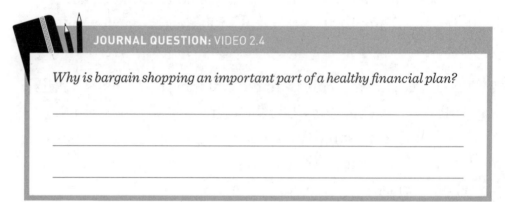

JOURNAL QUESTION: VIDEO 2.4

Why is bargain shopping an important part of a healthy financial plan?

_____

_____

_____

Don't Get Stuck With Seller's Remorse

"I have used your tips for negotiating, and they really work. But how can I get the most money for items I sell? I don't want to get ripped off, and I'm not sure how to go about this wisely. Do you have any tips?"

DAVE'S ANSWER: That's a good question, and you are right, you don't want to get ripped off when you sell things. First, don't play all your cards face up. The buyer will see that you really need the money. Make it clear that you have walk-away power as a seller. If you can't get the price you want, just walk away from the deal. In the case of antiques or collectible items, get them appraised and sell them slightly below that price. Showing the buyer that you are selling for less than the appraisal will make them feel like they are getting a deal. At the same time, you'll know it was a win-win deal because you were armed with information. Try these things, and like everything else, you will get better with practice.

Section 3:
Places to Find Great Deals

VIDEO 3.1

Another thing you can do is _____ something of value,
either goods or just your _____. When it comes
to specific places to find great deals, we can give you some
ideas. But remember, the trick is to be a little creative.
There really isn't a "one-size-fits-all" spot to find good
deals, so you'll have to learn the basics and then apply them
to your own location.

Where to Find Great Deals

1. _____: Typically, private sellers aren't
   trying to make a sale for profit; they're just trying to
   get some money out of the stuff they don't need or want
   anymore. Also, they are usually motivated and willing
   to negotiate for a lower price because the stuff is in
   their way. This makes for a win-win situation.

2. _____ **sales and public** _____: You
   can find great deals at these places, but you have to be
   careful. It's easy to get excited and end up paying more
   than retail for things. It's best to be prepared. Before
   bidding at an auction, you should know exactly what
   you're bidding on, how much it's worth, and what you're
   willing to pay. Then don't go past that line.

3. **Couponing:** The trick to coupons is to only use them
   on the items you need to buy.

BARTER is the exchange
of goods or services
without the use of money;
to trade.

**SIMPLE TIPS ON STORE
RETURN POLICIES**

Store return policies must
balance two purposes—
customer service and
profits. While stores don't
want to lose customers
over restrictive return
policies, they also need to
control costs by restricting
returns. Here are some
tips for store returns:

1. Familiarize yourself with
   the store's return policy
   prior to your purchase.

2. Hold on to your receipts.

3. Keep the labels and
   price tags on the item.

4. Don't delay. There
   is usually a time
   restriction included in
   store return policies.

TIME Business & Money

✦ Everyday Bargain Hunting Really Adds Up!

"I've heard you teach people to always watch for deals and ask for bargains on whatever they want to buy. Have you ever totaled up how much money you've saved in a single year by bargaining?"

DAVE'S ANSWER: No, I haven't. That might be a fun experiment to try sometime. I do know that one year my wife added up all of the money she saved by using coupons at the grocery store, and it came to more than $600 that year—just by using coupons to buy things we were going to buy anyway. Seeing those savings really made an impact on how we feel about bargain hunting and using coupons to save money.

⊕

You may not be the bargain-hunting, negotiating type, but if you're going to make the most of your money, you'll have to start looking for ways to save money by shopping for big bargains.

Where to Find Great Deals *(Continued)*

4. _____ _____: You can always find good deals at garage sales.

5. **Repo lot:** You can get good deals on cars. Again, you need to do your homework to know what you're buying and what it's worth. You also need to be willing to compromise on things like the color of the car.

6. _____ _____: This is one of the best places to hone your bargain-buying skills!

7. **Refunds and rebates:** Always follow up with refunds or rebates on purchases. Those dollars can add up!

8. _____: Avoid foreclosure sales until you are really educated on the process. But you can find good deals on foreclosed homes.

9. _____ **shops:** These items are cleared with the police department and are highly regulated. Pawn shops are great places to buy things.

10. Online _____: While there is a possibility of getting burned, it's also possible to find great deals.

11. _____ **ads:** These will link you to individual sellers.

12. **Consignment sales:** You can either buy at a discount or sell your used items through consignment.

13. **Conventions:** Vendors at conventions and trade shows are virtually willing to give their stuff away because they don't want to pack it up and take it back home!

JOURNAL QUESTION: VIDEO 3.1

Have you ever used social media to get a great deal on something?

_____

_____

_____

How to Help Stretch Your Hard-Earned Money

1. **Keep your eye on the calendar.** If you buy your winter clothes in the summer and your summer clothes in the winter, you can literally save hundreds. Even if you buy a car or house during the off seasons, you can save big. That whole supply-and-demand thing really is true!

2. **Get outdated technology.** Be willing to buy last year's models of TVs, computers and digital cameras, and you can save tons. Chances are the bells and whistles added to the latest versions aren't worth the extra money!

3. **Comparison shop.** You may always shop at one particular store, but venture out to find big bargains at stores you may have never visited before. Discount stores and second-hand shops are fantastic places to find deals! You can even hop online to find sites that compare products and stores to help you find the best value.

4. **Make a deal.** Don't be afraid to negotiate for a lower price. If you're shopping with cash, your chances of making a sweet deal are a lot better.

5. **Buy off-brands when possible.** Don't be married to a label. If the product serves the purpose and has comparable quality, save some money by buying a less popular brand.

Chapter Summary

 ## Check for Understanding

Now it's time to check your learning! Go back to the Before You Begin section for this chapter. Place a checkmark next to the learning outcomes you've mastered and complete the "after" column of the Measure Your Progress section.

 ## Build On What You've Learned

It's time to review "The Lucky Seven" rules of negotiation. Fill in the graphic organizer below.

1. _____

2. _____

3. _____

7. _____

Rules of Negotiation

4. _____

6. _____

5. _____

 ## Big Ideas

The following Big Ideas are intended to provide clear focus and purpose to the lessons. Read each statement and think about how what you've learned will affect your current and future decisions. Then, in the space provided, write an "I believe" statement for each of the Big Ideas.

» It's okay to negotiate!

_____

» When negotiating, be patient and honest.

_____

» Be a wise consumer.

_____

⚡ Take Action Challenge

Wise consumers always do a cost-benefit analysis before making a big purchase. This just means you analyze the costs and benefits of your purchase. Let's say you receive $250 in birthday cash and are trying to decide if you should use it to buy a new phone. Determine whether each statement below is a cost or benefit of your purchase. Then write a statement about whether you would choose to make the purchase or not, and why.

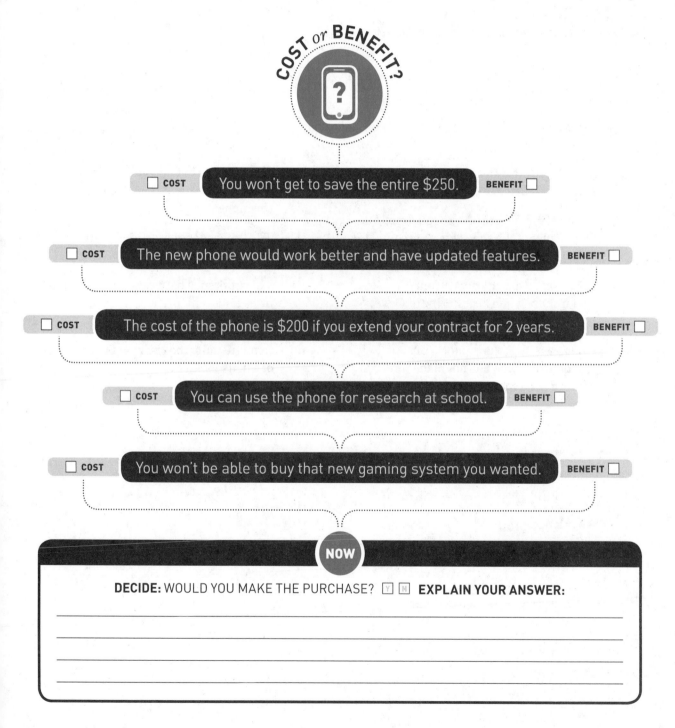

COST or **BENEFIT?**

☐ COST   You won't get to save the entire $250.   BENEFIT ☐

☐ COST   The new phone would work better and have updated features.   BENEFIT ☐

☐ COST   The cost of the phone is $200 if you extend your contract for 2 years.   BENEFIT ☐

☐ COST   You can use the phone for research at school.   BENEFIT ☐

☐ COST   You won't be able to buy that new gaming system you wanted.   BENEFIT ☐

NOW

DECIDE: WOULD YOU MAKE THE PURCHASE? ☐Y ☐N   **EXPLAIN YOUR ANSWER:**

_____

_____

_____

_____

Money in Review

Matching
Match the following terms to the correct definition below.

Ⓐ Foreclosure   Ⓓ Cost-Benefit Analysis   Ⓖ Estate Sale

Ⓑ Markup   Ⓔ Auction   Ⓗ Integrity

Ⓒ Walk-Away Power   Ⓕ Consignment Shop   Ⓘ Negotiate

---

1. _____ Having to do with a person's honesty and moral attributes

2. _____ Retail store where people sell items and the owner of the shop gets a percentage of the sale

3. _____ The ability to walk away from a purchase when negotiating

4. _____ Process by which the holder of a mortgage sells the property of a homeowner who has not made interest and/or principal payments on time as stipulated in the mortgage contract

5. _____ A public sale in which property or items of merchandise are sold to the highest bidder

6. _____ The process of quantifying costs and benefits of a decision

7. _____ The difference between the wholesale price and retail price

8. _____ Type of yard sale with more items, usually the entire contents of a household

9. _____ To bargain for a lower price

Illustration
Draw a picture representation of each of the following terms.

Wise Consumer

The Power of Cash

Multiple Choice

Circle the correct answer.

10. Using cash gives you more bargaining power than using credit.
    - Ⓐ True
    - Ⓑ False

11. Being married (or emotionally attached) to a purchase will cause you to lose bargaining power.
    - Ⓐ True
    - Ⓑ False

12. Getting the best deal on a purchase involves doing all of the following except:
    - Ⓐ Having patience
    - Ⓑ Being first in line for a new product
    - Ⓒ Negotiating
    - Ⓓ Shopping around to find the best deal

13. Which of the following is typically *not* a good place to find a deal?
    - Ⓐ Consignment shops
    - Ⓑ Individuals
    - Ⓒ Mall
    - Ⓓ Online auctions

14. Which of the following describes why using cash is a great bargaining tool?
    - Ⓐ Cash is visual.
    - Ⓑ Cash has immediacy.
    - Ⓒ Cash is emotional.
    - Ⓓ All of the above

Short Answer

Respond in the space provided.

15. Summarize the benefits of being a wise consumer.

16. Explain how walk-away power can be used as a negotiating tool.

17. What role does research play in getting good deals on purchases?

18. Why is honesty an important component of bargaining?

19. Describe the cost benefit of buying slightly outdated products.

What do other high school students know about investing?

We asked high school students to describe the weirdest get-rich-quick scheme they've ever heard of.

....

"Someone told me that I could get rich selling food door to door. After three days of embarrassment, I ended up only $5 richer."

Junior, Michigan

"I know about a chain letter where you put $1 in an envelope, include six addresses, and send it out to the top address. Eventually people are supposed to send you $1 each."

Junior, Alabama

"People think you can go to Hollywood and become a street performer until a big-time producer discovers you and you become a rich actor."

Junior, Missouri

"I've heard people say you can go to Alaska and work in a canning plant to get rich."

Senior, Wyoming

Investing and Retirement

44%

of teens would like their parents to talk more about how to invest money.*

75%

of teens say that learning more about money management, including budgeting, saving and investing, is one of their top priorities.*

AS YOU CONSIDER a good time to begin investing and retirement planning, think back to Ben and Arthur in Chapter 2. The fact is, you want to start planning and preparing for your financial future *now*! Dave's friend and best-selling author Zig Ziglar once said, "If you aim at nothing, you will hit it every time." Remember, the sooner you start investing, the sooner your money can begin to work for you! The magic of compound interest works best when given lots of time to do its thing.

* Teens & Money Survey, Charles Schwab

Before You Begin

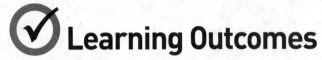

Learning Outcomes

Once you've completed this chapter's videos, you will be asked to return to this list and place a checkmark next to the items you've mastered.

Section 1: Investing 101

☐ Explain how investing builds wealth and helps meet financial goals.

☐ Examine the relationship between diversification and risk.

☐ Identify regulatory agencies and their functions.

Section 2: Types of Investments

☐ Evaluate investment alternatives: money markets, bonds, single stocks, mutual funds, annuities and real estate.

☐ Explain the Rule of 72.

☐ Identify different types of retirement plans.

☐ Explain how taxes affect the rate of return on investments.

☐ Understand how pre-tax and after-tax investments work.

☐ Understand how the stock market works.

☐ Be familiar with the various retirement account tax treatments.

☐ Develop a plan for investing; describe how to buy and sell investments.

Section 3: Employer Benefits & Retirement Plans

☐ Analyze the components of an employer benefits package.

☐ Explain how compound interest works.

Key Terms

Get to know the language of money.

» **Diversification:** The practice of dividing the money a person invests between several different types of investments in order to lower risk

» **Investing:** The process of setting money aside to increase wealth over time for long-term financial goals such as retirement

» **Investment:** Account or arrangement in which a person puts his/her money for long-term growth; invested money should not be used for a suggested minimum of five years

» **Liquidity:** Quality of an asset that permits it to be converted quickly into cash without loss of value; availability of money

» **Portfolio:** A list of your investments

» **Risk:** Degree of uncertainty of return on an asset; in business, the likelihood of loss or reduced profit

» **Risk-Return Ratio:** Relationship of substantial reward compared to the amount of risk taken

» **Share:** Piece of ownership in a company, mutual fund or other investment

» **Stocks:** Securities that represent part ownership or equity in a corporation

» **Tax-Favored Dollars:** Money that is invested, either tax deferred or tax free, within a retirement plan

Measure Your Progress

Before watching the video, read each statement below and mark whether you agree or disagree in the "Before" column. Then, after watching the video, do it again using the "After" column to see if you changed your mind on any statement.

BEFORE			AFTER	
Agree	Disagree		Agree	Disagree
☐	☐	1. You can start investing with a small amount of money.	☐	☐
☐	☐	2. The more sophisticated the investment, the more money you get in return.	☐	☐
☐	☐	3. With virtually all investments, as the risk goes up, so does the potential return.	☐	☐
☐	☐	4. It's difficult to find an investment with a long-term record that averages 12%.	☐	☐
☐	☐	5. It is okay to borrow money if you are going to invest it.	☐	☐

JOURNAL QUESTIONS: INTRODUCTION

List your initial thoughts about investing. What do you want to learn about investing?

_____

_____

_____

CHAPTER 8

Section 1: Investing 101

5 THE FIFTH FOUNDATION
Build Wealth and Give

REMEMBER, the goal is to build wealth. You can and should save money for your emergency fund and for purchases. Then, once you're sure that you have your post-secondary education paid for, you should begin to invest a portion of your income. How does investing build wealth? Investing allows your money to work for you. You'll be amazed at how your money, when invested wisely, can begin to grow!

Investing will help you reach your long-term financial goals, such as retirement. In this chapter, we are going to give you the tools to achieve lifelong financial well-being.

VIDEO 1.1

Basic Rules of Investing

» **Keep it _____, stupid!** Investing doesn't have to be complicated, and there is really no trick to it. Never invest money in anything you do not understand!

As a young adult, what is the most important thing you can invest in?

_____

_____

_____

VIDEO 1.2

Basic Rules of Investing *(Continued)*

» **Never invest purely for _____ _____.**
If what you are investing in is primarily a tax deal, then
it is probably not a good investment. Your motivation
should be to make money, not save on taxes.

» **Never invest using _____ money.** Never
borrow money, period. Borrowing money is a particularly
bad idea for an investment because it increases the
risk of the investment. And if you lose the money, you are
still left with payments on it.

Diversification

❝ *Here's the thing to remember: Money is like manure. Left in one
pile, it stinks—spread around, it will grow things."*
DAVE RAMSEY

» **_____** is a risk-management
technique that mixes a wide variety of investments within
a portfolio. The rationale behind this technique is that
having a variety of investments will yield higher returns
and lower risk.

**THROUGHOUT THE
STOCK MARKET'S
HISTORY**

100% of 15-year periods
made money.

*"Diversification is a
protection against
ignorance."*

WARREN BUFFETT
Famous American investor

People with a bachelor's
degree or higher have
unemployment rates
that are about **half the
unemployment rate** of
people with just a high
school diploma.

Bureau of Labor Statistics

A bachelor's degree on
average increases lifetime
income by $1.2 million
as compared with a high
school diploma.

Journal of Student Financial Aid

Risk Return Ratio and Liquidity

» The risk return ratio is used by investors to compare the expected return of an investment to the amount of risk they take to get the return. This ratio is calculated mathematically by dividing the amount you stand to lose if the price goes down (risk) by the amount of profit you expect to make (return). With virtually all investments, as the _____ goes up, so does the potential return.
5

» Liquidity refers to assets that can be easily bought or sold (liquid assets). When discussing investments, _____ is availability. As there is more liquidity, there is typically _____ return.
6   7

📊 The Power of Diversification

What would happen if two people each invested $10,000 (with interest compounded monthly) for 25 years and one diversifies but the other does not?

Investor 1 invests:
$10,000 at 7% return

Investor 2 invests:
$2,000 and loses it all
$2,000 in his cookie jar
$2,000 at 5% return
$2,000 at 10% return
$2,000 at 15% return

The difference is almost $59,000!

Investor 2: $116,164 because of diversification!

Investor 1: $57,254 without diversification!

« $120K
« $110K
« $100K
« $90K
« $80K
« $70K
« $60K
« $50K
« $40K
« $30K
« $20K
« $10K

Section 2: Types of Investments

VIDEO 2.1

Money Markets

» A market in which short-term financial instruments such as certificates of deposit (CD), Treasury bills, commercial papers and bank deposits are traded. New York is the major money market, followed by London and Tokyo.

» A CD is a _____ _____ _____, typically at a bank. It is a savings account with a slightly higher interest rate because of a longer savings commitment (i.e. six months, one year, etc.).

» A money market account is a _____ -risk bank savings account with check-writing privileges.

U.S. SECURITIES AND EXCHANGE COMMISSION (SEC): The government agency responsible for regulating the stock market. It was created in 1934 to increase public trust after the 1929 stock market crash and the years of the Great Depression.

FEDERAL DEPOSIT INSURANCE CORPORATION (FDIC): The U.S. federal agency that insures deposits in commercial banks. It was created to restore public trust in banks after the 1929 stock market crash. FDIC replaced the former Federal Savings and Loan Insurance Corporation in 1989.

FEDERAL RESERVE: The central (federal) banking system of the United States

INTERNAL REVENUE SERVICE (IRS): A U.S. federal agency responsible for collecting taxes and for the interpretation and enforcement of the Internal Revenue Code (laws)

Money Markets *(Continued)*

» These are great for your _____ _____ due to their **liquidity** (accessibility) and **stability**.

» Money market investments are low-risk, and therefore, have low returns.

Single Stocks

» Single stock investing carries an extremely _____ degree of risk.

» When you buy stock, you are buying a small piece of _____ in the company.

» Your return comes as the company increases in _____ or pays you, its owner, some of the profits (dividends).

Bonds

» A bond is a _____ instrument by which the company owes you money; a form of I.O.U. The company that issued the bond makes regular interest payments to the bond holder and promises to pay back or redeem the face value of the bond at a specified point in the future (maturity date).

» Your return is the fluctuation in price and the _____ rate paid.

» Few individuals do well with _____ _____ purchases.

» Examples include **Treasury bonds** (a bond issued by the U.S. government that bears fixed interest) and **savings bonds** (in the United States, a bond that can be bought from the federal government).

» Bonds are typically low risk and low return on investment.

JOURNAL QUESTION: VIDEO 2.1

Explain why single stocks carry a high degree of risk.

_____

_____

_____

VIDEO 2.2

Mutual Funds

» A mutual fund is an investment vehicle made up of a pool of _____ collected from many investors for the purpose of investing in securities such as stocks, bonds, money market instruments and similar assets.
  ₁₇

» Portfolio managers manage the pool or _____ and attempt to increase the value of the fund in order to produce capital gains and income for the fund's investors.
  ₁₈

» A mutual fund portfolio is structured and maintained to match the investment objectives stated in its prospectus.

» Your _____ comes as the value of the fund is increased.
  ₁₉

WAR BONDS (ALSO KNOWN AS DEFENSE BONDS): The last time the United States issued war bonds was during World War II. Issued by the U.S. government, they were named war bonds after the Japanese attack on Pearl Harbor, Dec. 7, 1941. The purpose of war bonds was to finance military operations during war time. The bonds yielded a mere 2.9% return after a 10-year maturity.

DIVIDEND: Distribution of a portion of a company's earnings, decided by the board of directors, to a class of its shareholders; generally distributed in the form of cash or stock

"October. This is one of the peculiarly dangerous months to speculate in stocks. The others are July, January, September, April, November, May, March, June, December, August, and February."

MARK TWAIN
American author

THE STANDARD DIVERSIFICATION PLAN

25% Growth Stock Mutual Fund (Mid-Cap): Fund that buys stock in medium-sized companies that have experienced some growth and are still expanding

25% Growth and Income Stock Mutual Fund (Large-Cap): Fund comprised of large, well-established companies

25% Aggressive Growth Stock Mutual Fund (Small-Cap): Fund that seeks to provide maximum long-term capital growth from stocks of primarily smaller companies; the most volatile fund

25% International Stock Mutual Fund: Fund that contains international or overseas companies

Mutual Funds *(Continued)*

» The main advantage of mutual funds is that they give small investors access to professionally managed, diversified portfolios of stocks, bonds and other securities.

» Mutual funds are good _____ -term investments. [20]

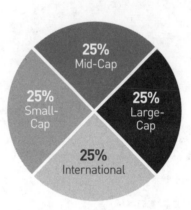

» A mutual fund portfolio that is properly diversified will have investment dollars spread equally among four different classes of financial assets. Remember, the overall diversification of your mutual fund portfolio means lower risk. We recommend 25% in each of these four classes. Compared to other investments, if you use this strategy, you would have moderate risk.

JOURNAL QUESTION: VIDEO 2.2

Which are a better investment, stocks or mutual funds? Explain your answer.

_____

_____

_____

Qualified Plans

A **qualified plan** is a _____-_____ investment
(which means it has special tax treatment). ₂₁

Examples of qualified plans include:

Individual Retirement Arrangement (IRA)

When it comes to IRAs, everyone with an _____
_____ is eligible. ₂₂

Remember: IRA is not a type of investment at a bank.
It is the _____ _____ on virtually any type
of investment. ₂₃

Roth IRA

» The Roth IRA is funded with after-tax money, which allows
you to use the money in your Roth tax free in retirement.

» After five years, you can make _____-_____, penalty-
free withdrawals of earnings under these conditions: ₂₄

1. Over 59 and a half years old

2. Because of death or disability

3. First-time home purchase

Investing money pretax is different than investing money
after tax. There are no taxes when you cash out a Roth, so it
forces you to invest more.

✱ **NOTE:** There are limits (based on total household income) to the annual contribution amounts.
These amounts can change based on inflation. Go to **foundationsU.com** to check out the current
contribution phase-out limits. As an adult, you should invest 15% of your household income into
Roth IRAs and pretax retirement plans.

KNOW THE RULE OF 72!
The Rule of 72 is a quick
way to calculate the length
of time it will take to double
a sum of money. Divide 72
by the expected interest
rate to determine the
number of years (i.e. 72
divided by 8% = 9 years).

THE ROTH IRA is named
for Sen. William Roth of
Delaware, who authored
this section of the Taxpayer
Relief Act of 1997.

Make the Most of Your Inheritance

"I'm 21 and currently in college. Next month, I'll be receiving an inheritance of about $40,000. I don't know anything about stocks, mutual funds or CDs, but I don't want to lose all this money. I don't have any debt, so what should I do?"

DAVE'S ANSWER: I'm glad you're asking questions. One of the fastest ways to lose money is to put it into an investment that you don't understand.

You don't need to change your major to finance to make this happen, but you do have a $40,000 responsibility that you didn't have before. For now, a simple savings account is fine. I'd park $30,000 in there and just forget about it for a while. Then use $5,000 to set up an emergency fund and maybe blow $5,000 on some things just for you. After all, spending and having fun with money is still important!

But here's something to think about once you've educated yourself on investing. If you put that remaining $30,000 in a good growth stock mutual fund, by the time you're ready to retire you'll be looking at about $5.5 million.

Talk about being able to retire with dignity and change your family tree!

EDUCATION SAVINGS PLAN (529 PLAN): A savings plan operated by a state or educational institution designed to help families set aside funds for future college costs. It is named after Section 529 of the Internal Revenue Code, which created these types of savings plans in 1996.

TAX-DEFERRED: The key advantage of stashing money in a tax-deferred retirement account isn't just that you'll pay less to the government this year, but that your investments will compound faster than in a taxable account. The result is usually a larger retirement nest egg even after the funds are taxed upon withdrawal.

Annuities

» An **annuity** is a _____ account sold by an _____ company, designed to provide payments to the holder at specified intervals, usually after retirement.

» The holder is taxed at the time of distribution or withdrawal, making this a tax-deferred arrangement.

» _____ annuities have a low interest rate of around 5%; they have high fees and are a bad investment option.

» _____ annuities are mutual funds sheltered by the annuity, which allows the mutual fund to grow _____ _____.

Real Estate

» You should have lots of _____ before using real estate as an _____. Real estate is usually held as part of a larger portfolio and is generally considered an alternative investment.

» Real estate is land plus anything permanently fixed to it, including buildings and natural resources.

» Real estate is the _____ liquid consumer investment.

» Benefits of investing in real estate include higher returns for a given level of risk. By adding real estate to a portfolio, you could maintain your portfolio returns while decreasing risk.

» Another benefit of real estate is your ability to influence its value. As a tangible asset, an investor can increase the value of the property through a variety of improvements.

» Other special considerations when investing in real estate:

- It is costly to buy, sell and maintain.

- It requires management.

- It can be difficult to acquire.

- The investment market is cyclical based on supply and demand.

Horrible Investments

» **Gold**: Gold has a 50-year track record of 4.1% returns. That's about the rate of inflation.

» **Commodities**: _____ are agricultural or mining products. All commodities are traded, but since no one really wants to transport all those heavy materials, what is actually traded are commodities *futures contracts*— an agreement to buy or sell a commodity at a specific date in the future at a specific price. Both commodities and futures are bad investments because they result in price distortions and are highly volatile.

» **Day trading**: This is the buying and selling of stock purchases each day through the practice of **speculation**. Evidence shows the vast majority of investors lose money in day trading.

» **Viaticals**: This is when someone with a terminal disease sells his life insurance policy for less than face value. The buyer then cashes in the full amount at the original owner's death. There are a lot of scam artists surrounding this type of investment, and investors often incur legal risks.

What Is the Stock Market?

The stock market is a generic term that encompasses the trading of securities. This trading takes place in stock exchanges. There are three major stock exchanges in the United States:

1. Formed in 1792, the New York Stock Exchange (NYSE) is the largest organized stock exchange in the United States.

2. The American Stock Exchange (AMEX) was known before 1951 as the American Curb Exchange. That's because trading was conducted on the curb of Wall and Broad streets in New York City. The American Stock Exchange has less stringent listing requirements than the NYSE, so it attracts many smaller companies.

3. Another of the major stock exchanges, NASDAQ stands for the National Association of Securities Dealers Automated Quotation System. Unlike the NYSE and the AMEX, there isn't any physical location for the exchange; trading is done by computer. The American Stock Exchange and NASDAQ have merged but maintain their own names and identities.

The overall performance of the stock market is evaluated in many different ways. **The Dow Jones Industrial Average** is one measure of the stock market.

A **security** is a financial asset (such as a stock or bond) that can be bought and sold; a tradable financial asset.

"Bear vs. Bull Market"

The terms bull market and bear market describe upward (bullish) and downward (bearish) market trends.

> **JOURNAL QUESTION:** VIDEO 2.3
>
> *What is real estate? Why is it considered an investment?*
>
> _____
>
> _____
>
> _____

Anticipating the Future

"I am 19 years old and working in my family's business. I live at home with my parents, I'm not in college, and my car is completely paid for. How should I start saving for a house and retirement? I want to make sure I am doing everything I can to avoid financial problems in the future. What do I need to do?"

DAVE'S ANSWER: Your first goal should be to save three to six months of your income (since you don't really have any expenses). This will be your full emergency fund. Then you should save for anything you plan on doing in the next few years, like getting married or buying a home.

On top of that, you should invest into a Roth IRA. The current contribution limit is $5,500 per year, which comes out to about $458 per month. You can do less than that, but not more. If you start that now, you will be extremely wealthy when you retire.

Section 3: Employer Benefits and Retirement Plans

VIDEO 3.1

As you enter the workforce, it's a good idea to be familiar with the components of an **employee benefits package**. Employee benefits are various _____-_____ ₃₄ compensations provided to employees in addition to their normal wages or salaries. The purpose of employee benefits is to increase the financial security of staff members, and in doing so, improve worker retention across the organization.

Common employee benefits are retirement plans, savings plans, _____, leave (sick, vacation, etc.), stock ₃₅ purchase, educational reimbursement, incentive plans and cafeteria plans. In addition to considering salary when you are offered employment with a company, you should also evaluate the employer's benefits package.

WHAT'S THE DIFFERENCE BETWEEN SAVING AND INVESTING?

Any money set aside for five years or less is considered saving.

Money set aside for more than five years is considered investing.

Employer Retirement Plans

» **Simplified Employee Pension Plan (SEP):** A self-employed person may deduct up to 15% of their net profit on the business by investing in a SEP.

» _____ is a retirement savings plan offered by a corporation to its employees. The employee contributes money to the 401(k) from his/her gross pay, and the money in the account grows tax deferred. In some cases, employers will match the employee's contribution, but you should fund your plan whether your company matches or not.

» **403(b)** is found in _____ organizations such as churches, hospitals and schools.

» **457** is deferred compensation, which means you are deferring or putting off compensation. Usually this is available for _____ employees.

» Do not use a **Guaranteed Investment Contract (GIC)** or bond funds to fund your plan. This is like a CD inside of your 401(k). You will only make about 3–4%, and it will not help you win long term.

» **Pre-tax contributions** are taken from your gross income before taxes. Taxes are due upon withdrawal.

» **After-tax contributions** are taken from your net income after taxes. No taxes are due upon withdrawal.

WHERE DOES THE TERM 401(K) COME FROM?

401(k) refers to the section of the tax code that discusses this sort of retirement plan, as do 403(b) and 457.

Rollovers

If you leave a job and have money saved in your employer's retirement plan, always roll that money into an IRA using a direct rollover, which allows you to avoid taxes and penalties.

Retirement Loans

Never borrow on your _____ _____. *Never!* Even though you pay yourself back some interest, it is nowhere close to what you would have earned if you had left the money in the investment.

 ## Can Anyone Become a Millionaire?

The Power of Compound Interest

Whether you have never stepped foot in a bank or you are actively saving and investing for your future, all it takes is a little effort and a lot of patience to become confident in your financial decisions. One awesome thing that you can take advantage of is compound interest. It may sound like an intimidating term, but it really isn't once you know what it means. Here's a little secret: Compound interest is a millionaire's best friend. It's really free money. Seriously. But don't take our word for it!

Let's take another look at the story of Ben and Arthur from Chapter 2. Remember that Ben invested $16,000 over eight years, and Arthur invested $78,000 over 39 years. Believe it or not, Ben came out ahead . . . $700,000 ahead! How did he do it? Starting early is the key. He put in less money but started eight years earlier. That's compound interest for you! It turns $16,000 into almost $2.3 million! Since Ben invested earlier, the compound interest kicked in sooner.

What You Can Do Now

The trick is to start as soon as possible. You should start investing as soon as you have your college education funded. A survey by Charles Schwab found that 24% of young adults believe that because they are young, saving money isn't important. Looks like we just blew that theory out of the water! That same survey also discovered that only 2% of young adults say they know how to invest money to make it grow. Why not change that statistic and learn how to become a smart investor with your money? Remember, waiting just means you make less money in the end. So get moving!

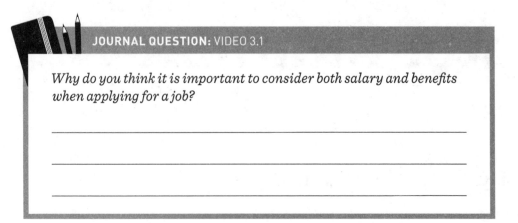

Why do you think it is important to consider both salary and benefits when applying for a job?

_____

_____

_____

Budget Builder

So you're ready to invest? Your investment dollars will need to be part of your monthly budget. Go to foundationsU.com/8 to update your budget!

Chapter Summary

 ## Check for Understanding

Now it's time to check your learning! Go back to the Before You Begin section for this chapter. Place a checkmark next to the learning outcomes you've mastered and complete the "after" column of the Measure Your Progress section.

 ## Build On What You've Learned

So you currently don't have any money to invest? Brainstorm at least five job options for teens and list them below.

1. _____

2. _____

3. _____

4. _____

5. _____

 ## Big Ideas

The following Big Ideas are intended to provide clear focus and purpose to the lessons. Read each statement and think about how what you've learned will affect your current and future decisions. Then, in the space provided, write an "I believe" statement for each of the Big Ideas.

» Invest to build wealth and meet financial goals.

_____

» When investing, diversification lowers risk.

_____

» Employee benefits often include insurance and retirement plans.

_____

⚡ Take Action Challenge

1 **Review:** Risk Return Ratio

The risk return ratio applies to any type of investment. Any time you invest money into something there is a risk, whether large or small, that you might not get your money back. In turn, you expect a return, which compensates you for bearing this risk. In theory, the higher the risk, the more you should receive for holding the investment, and the lower the risk, the less you should receive.

2 **Directions**

Plot the following investments on the risk return continuum below. If you've forgotten the level of risk for any of the investment types, refer to earlier in the chapter for review.

Ⓐ Money Market Accounts	Ⓓ Mutual Funds
Ⓑ Single Stocks	Ⓔ Fixed Annuities
Ⓒ Bonds	Ⓕ Real Estate

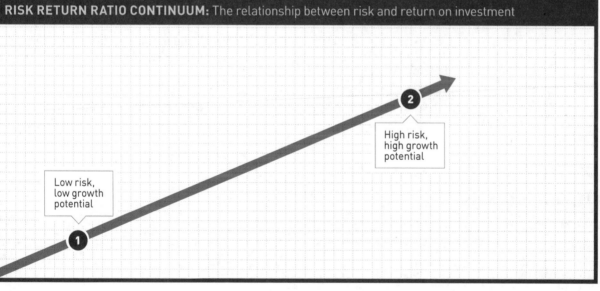

RISK RETURN RATIO CONTINUUM: The relationship between risk and return on investment

ANNUAL RETURN

High risk, high growth potential

Low risk, low growth potential

RISK AMOUNT

Money in Review

Matching

Match the following terms to the correct definition below.

A 401(k)	**D** Liquidity	**G** Risk
B Investment	**E** Mutual Fund	**H** Share
C IRA	**F** Portfolio	

1. _____ A list of your investments

2. _____ Quality of an asset that permits it to be converted quickly into cash without loss of value

3. _____ A piece of ownership in a company, mutual fund or other investment

4. _____ A retirement savings plan offered by a corporation to its employees; the employee contributes money from his/her gross pay, and the money grows tax deferred

5. _____ Account or arrangement in which one would put their money for long-term growth

6. _____ Degree of uncertainty of return on an asset

7. _____ Pool of money managed by an investment company and invested in multiple companies

8. _____ Tax-deferred arrangement for individuals with earned income; individual retirement arrangement

Illustration

Draw a picture representation of each of the following terms.

Diversification

Stock

Multiple Choice

Circle the correct answer.

9. A single stock would be a good place to keep your emergency fund.
    - Ⓐ True
    - Ⓑ False

10. Diversification lowers risk with investing.
    - Ⓐ True
    - Ⓑ False

11. Long-term investments properly diversified include the following mutual funds:
    - Ⓐ Growth, growth and income, bond, aggressive growth
    - Ⓑ Growth, balanced, international, bond
    - Ⓒ International, bond, aggressive growth, growth
    - Ⓓ Growth, growth and income, international, aggressive growth

12. Which of the following is a good investment option?
    - Ⓐ Gold
    - Ⓑ Viaticals
    - Ⓒ Futures
    - Ⓓ Mutual funds

13. Which statement is true about liquidity?
    - Ⓐ The less liquid the investment, the less return
    - Ⓑ The more liquid an investment, the more return
    - Ⓒ The more liquid an investment, the less return
    - Ⓓ Both a and b

Short Answer

Respond in the space provided.

14. Explain why you should never invest using borrowed money.

15. Explain the risk return ratio.

16. Why do single stocks carry a high degree of risk? Why do mutual funds carry less risk?

17. What is the Rule of 72? How is it calculated?

18. Is real estate a liquid investment? Explain your answer.

CHAPTER 9

What do other high school students know about insurance?

We asked teens to tell us why they think insurance is necessary.

....

"Insurance is something that will pay for medical help. It's money for any medical problems you will have now or in the future."

Junior, Mississippi

"There are different types of insurance to insure different things like your house or car. Then there is life insurance, which will help your family if you die."

Sophomore, Florida

"Everyone needs life insurance, which some people also call 'death insurance.'"

Senior, Missouri

"Insurance covers liability and protects you. It provides cash for accidental occurrences."

Senior, Florida

Insurance

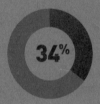

34%

of American renters have renter's insurance.[1]

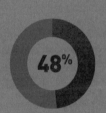

48%

of tenants incorrectly think a landlord's insurance will cover them if their property is destroyed due to fire, theft, etc.[2]

AS A HIGH SCHOOL STUDENT, insurance may not seem that important. However, it's incredibly important to be prepared for unexpected disasters. An illness, injury or car accident that occurs without the necessary insurance coverage can completely ruin your finances. Having an emergency fund and a budget and staying out of debt will help you win with money. But without the proper coverage, even the best financial plan can't save you from thousands of dollars of unexpected medical expenses. You never know what the future holds. As you get older, you'll find that you need insurance when you least expect it!

[1] ABC News
[2] InsuranceQuotes.com

Before You Begin

 ## Learning Outcomes

Once you've completed this chapter's videos, you will be asked to return to this list of learning outcomes and place a checkmark next to the items you've mastered.

Section 1: Protecting Your Wealth

☐ Explain why insurance is an essential part of a healthy financial plan.

☐ Identify ways to lower the cost of insurance premiums.

☐ Identify insurance for the types of risks that young adults might face.

Section 2: Basic Types of Coverage

☐ Identify common types of risks.

☐ Distinguish between necessary and unnecessary types of coverage.

☐ Understand the importance of identity theft protection.

☐ Understand the importance of property and liability protection.

Section 3: The Importance of Life Insurance

☐ Differentiate between term and cash value life insurance.

☐ Explain how one becomes self-insured.

☐ Examine the purpose and importance of a will.

Section 4: Insurance to Avoid

☐ Know what types of insurance to avoid and why.

 ## Key Terms

Get to know the language of money.

» **Beneficiary:** The recipient of assets passed on from the death of a friend or relative

» **Claim:** Paperwork filed with an insurance company in order to get them to cover a loss for someone they insure

» **Coverage:** Applies to the amount of protection you have through an insurance company in the event of a loss

» **Deductible:** Amount you must pay before you begin receiving any benefits from your insurance company

» **Liability:** The state or quality of being obligated according to law or equity

» **Out-of-pocket expense:** Specific amount of money that you pay when insurance only covers a portion of costs

» **Policy:** Describes the type of coverage in an insurance agreement

» **Premium:** Amount you pay monthly, quarterly, semiannually or annually to purchase different types of insurance

» **Will:** A legally enforceable declaration of how a person wishes his or her property to be distributed after death

Measure Your Progress

Before watching the video, read each statement below and mark whether you agree or disagree in the "Before" column. Then, after watching the video, do it again using the "After" column to see if you changed your mind on any statement.

BEFORE			AFTER	
Agree	Disagree		Agree	Disagree
☐	☐	1. Insurance rates can vary depending on the company, and I can save money if I shop around.	☐	☐
☐	☐	2. I must always have collision insurance on my automobile, even if it's an old car that's not worth much.	☐	☐
☐	☐	3. If an employer offers me health insurance but requires me to pay part of the premium, it is not a good deal, and I shouldn't get it.	☐	☐
☐	☐	4. I only need to have renter's insurance if I have a lot of valuable items.	☐	☐
☐	☐	5. Everyone should have life insurance.	☐	☐

JOURNAL QUESTION: INTRODUCTION

What do you think is the purpose of insurance?

_____

_____

_____

CHAPTER

Section 1:
Protecting Your Wealth

VIDEO 1.1

The Role of Insurance in Your Financial Plan

WE GET IT. Insurance may be one topic where you begin to yawn a little bit. Let's face it: No one really likes spending money on insurance. There are many other things that are more fun to spend money on. But, while we hope we never have to use it, insurance is a necessary part of a healthy financial plan. Why? Because insurance transfers the financial risk of life's major catastrophes. Chances are that something major and unexpected is going to happen at some point during your lifetime. Insurance will protect your wealth during those events.

» While paying insurance premiums may feel like you're losing money, in the end it really helps you _____ more of it. [1]

» It's important to remember that insurance is a financial product, which means that the buyer should beware. When the consumer is _____ [2] with _____, [3] the consumer makes different decisions.

» Insurance is an essential financial planning tool. You'll want to make sure you get only the coverage you need at the best possible price.

» The purpose of insurance is to _____ risk.

» Without proper insurance, certain losses can _____ you. Conventional wisdom says that you should transfer risk.

» Insurance puts an _____ over your life, the hard work that you've done, the money you've saved, and the money that you have to invest.

The 7 Basic Types of Coverage Needed

1. **Homeowner's or Renter's Insurance**

2. **Auto Insurance**

3. **Health Insurance**

4. **Disability Insurance** (when you are established in your career)

5. **Long-Term Care Insurance** (when you are 60 or older)

6. **Identity Theft Protection**

7. **Life Insurance** (when you have dependants who rely on your income)

Property and Casualty (P&C) insurance is a $442 billion industry (2011 net premiums written).

Insurance Information Institute

Thirty-five insurance companies are listed on the 2012 Fortune 500 annual ranking of America's largest corporations. Eighteen of these top companies are in the P&C insurance sector.

Fortune Magazine

Ways to Save Money on Your Premium

RAISE YOUR DEDUCTIBLE TO KEEP THE PREMIUMS DOWN. Calculate how much you're saving and compare that with the extra expense you will have if you suffer a loss. It has to be worth the cost to transfer risk.

Any time you're shopping for insurance, go to an independent insurance agent and let them shop among many different plans and companies.

Health, disability, auto, homeowner's, identity theft, long-term care and life insurance catch the big stuff. You handle the little stuff with an emergency fund and solid financial planning.

» If you have a full emergency fund, the best way to keep your premiums down is to raise your _____.

* **NOTE:** An emergency fund for high school and college students is typically $500 or more; for adults, it should be a full three to six months of living expenses.

» A deductible is what you have to pay out of pocket before the insurance company kicks in any money.

» Make sure you carry adequate liability. Liability covers property damage and medical bills if you're at fault in a car wreck or if someone gets hurt on your property.

» Consider dropping your collision on older cars. That's the insurance that pays to fix your own car.

JOURNAL QUESTION: VIDEO 1.1

Explain why insurance is an important part of your financial plan.

_____

_____

_____

Section 2:
Basic Types of Coverage

VIDEO 2.1

Basic Parts of Auto Insurance

Auto insurance protects you against financial loss if you are in a car accident or if something else causes damage to your car. Here are the basic components of an auto insurance policy:

» **Liability** covers medical costs and property damage of the other driver if you get in a wreck and it's your fault. It is the least expensive part of your car insurance. You should always get really good coverage limits.

WHAT KINDS OF INSURANCE DO I NEED AFTER HIGH SCHOOL?
After high school, you'll probably need to have four types of insurance:

1. Car

2. Health

3. Identity Theft

4. Renter's

 ### Need Another Reason to Pay Cash for Your Car?

"My car was recently totaled, but I had full-coverage insurance. The problem is the bank is asking for $3,000 in 30 days because I did not have gap insurance. What is gap insurance? I thought I would finally be done with these car payments because the insurance would take care of everything, but now I have this bill. What can I do?"

DAVE'S ANSWER: Gap insurance covers the difference between what you owe on a car and what the insurance company says it is worth. That is what happened to you. Your full-coverage policy paid for the current value of the car, but that is less than what you owe the bank. Since you no longer have the car as collateral, the bank is calling their note.

Gap insurance can be pretty expensive, which is another reason not to buy a new car on credit. The minute you drive off the car lot with a new car, it loses value and if you get into an accident, there will be a gap that you are responsible for unless you have this gap insurance. All you can do right now is pay the bank what you owe and move on, lesson learned.

Basic Parts of Auto Insurance *(Continued)*

» **Medical payment coverage** pays for all accident-related medical costs incurred by you or your family members within three years of an accident.

» **Collision insurance** covers damage to your car if it is hit by another car or object. If you owe money on your car, the lien holder will require collision coverage. It's still not a bad idea even if you own your car or if it's old. The insurance coverage will replace your car if totaled in a wreck—and you won't be stuck walking.

» **Comprehensive** coverage takes care of damage to your car not caused by a collision. If your car is stolen, damaged by fire, flood or hail for example, your policy will pay to repair or replace it.

» **Uninsured/underinsured motorist protection** covers your costs if you are injured by an uninsured motorist or if you are injured in a hit-and-run accident.

BREAK-EVEN ANALYSIS: Method used to evaluate the wisdom of a financial decision by determining the length of time it will take for the cost of the decision to be recouped

BEFORE DROPPING COLLISION ON YOUR CAR, CONSIDER THIS: Since collision insurance rates have dropped over the years, you'll want to do a break-even analysis to see how many years you'd need to go without a wreck for it to make sense. For example, if you have a $4,000 car and dropping collision would save you $800 a year on premiums, you'd need to go five years without a wreck to break even.

How Can I Get a Good Deal on Car Insurance as a Teen Driver?

» Get good grades. Insurance companies assume that if you're a responsible student you are more likely to be a responsible driver.

» Take a driver education class.

» Shop around. Insurance is a product! Make sure you are getting the best deal for your money.

» Stay on your parents' policy through college if possible in order to benefit from multi-car discounts.

According to the federal Centers for Disease Control and Prevention (CDC), crash rates per mile driven for 16- to 19-year-olds are four times higher than those of older drivers. This makes teen drivers the most expensive to insure.

Top Things to Know About Auto Insurance

1. **You're a statistic.** To an insurer, you're not a person—you're a set of risks. An insurer bases its decisions on your "risk factors," including some things that may seem unrelated to driving a car.

2. **Insurers differ.** Prices can vary from company to company. You can save money by comparison shopping.

3. **Don't just look at price.** A low price is no bargain if an insurer takes forever to service your claim. Research the insurer's record for claims service, as well as its financial stability.

4. **Go beyond the basics.** Although most states require only a minimum of liability coverage, you should look for a minimum coverage of $500,000.

5. **Demand discounts.** Insurers provide discounts to reward behavior that reduces risk. However, Americans waste $300 billion a year because they forget to ask for discounts!

6. **At claims time, your insurer isn't necessarily your friend.** Your idea of fair compensation may not match that of your insurer. Their job is to restore you financially. Your job is to prove your losses so that you get what you need.

7. **Prepare before you have to file a claim.** Keep your policy updated and reread it before you file a claim so there are no surprises.

Homeowner's and Renter's Insurance

When you're ready, the purchase of a home is likely one of the largest single purchases you will ever make. It will need to be protected through a homeowner's insurance policy. This policy will cover the costs of repairing or replacing your home in the event that it is damaged or destroyed by fire, storms, theft and a variety of other possible causes.

» Homeowner's insurance should be "guaranteed _____ cost" instead of extended replacement cost.

» When you are ready to move out of your parents' house, you need to have _____ insurance, which covers the _____ of the renter's apartment in the event of fire, storm or theft.

» _____ liability policies are a good buy once you have some assets. An umbrella policy gives you additional liability protection above your other policies.

JOURNAL QUESTION: VIDEO 2.1

What are some ways you can save on car insurance?

_____

_____

_____

Health Insurance

You may think that because you are young and healthy that health insurance is not necessary, but you'd be wrong. *Everyone* needs to have health insurance. Medical emergencies due to injury or illness can occur to anyone at any time. And with the ever-rising cost of health care, you need to be prepared.

Save on Your Health Insurance Premiums

» Just like with auto insurance, staying on your parents' health insurance policy until you're out of school and on your own will lower your costs.

» Increase your _____ and/or coinsurance amount.
12

» Increase your _____ - _____, but never decrease your maximum pay. Stop-loss is your maximum out-of-pocket expense.
13

» See if an _____, a Health Savings Account, would make sense for your situation.
14

» The HSA is a _____ - _____ savings account for medical expenses that works with a high-deductible insurance policy.
15

GROUP VS. INDIVIDUAL HEALTH PLANS

A **group health plan** is an employee benefit plan maintained by an employer or by an organization (such as a union) that provides medical care for participants and/or their dependents through insurance, reimbursement or otherwise. The two main advantages of group plans are that they **spread the risk over the entire group** to keep premiums stable and they **cannot deny you coverage** based on health issues.

A smaller percentage of Americans are covered through **individual health insurance plans that are purchased in the open market**—meaning that they are not provided by a group or an employer. People generally choose this option because they are self-employed, retired early, or do not have a spouse with group coverage. **These plans are sometimes more expensive than group plans** and **can deny coverage** if you have a history of poor health.

On average, the cost of a trip to the hospital via ambulance is anywhere from $350 to as much as $2,000.

howmuchisit.org

In a recent study, researchers found that the average charge for an emergency room visit came out to $1,233, which is 40% higher than the average American rent right now, $871 per month.

The Washington Post

The Basic Components of Health Insurance

» **Basic health insurance** policies cover hospital, surgical and physician expenses.

» **Major medical expense insurance** covers medical costs that are in excess of those covered by basic health insurance.

» **Dental and eye insurance** plans cover only expenses for dental work and expenses related to eye care.

» A **copayment** is an amount of money you pay to help cover a portion of your medical costs. Copayments may be a set amount or a percentage of the total cost, depending on your insurance policy.

» A **deductible** is the amount you must pay before you begin receiving any benefits from your insurance company.

✱ **NOTE:** There are currently many changes going on in our health care system. It's important for you to stay educated on these changes and how they relate to your health insurance needs.

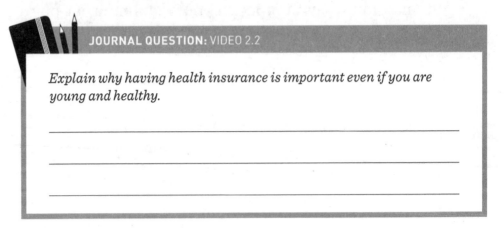

JOURNAL QUESTION: VIDEO 2.2

Explain why having health insurance is important even if you are young and healthy.

Long-Term Care Insurance

Long-term care is care that you need if you can no longer perform everyday tasks by yourself. Causes may be chronic illness, injury, disability or advanced age. Your odds of needing this level of care increase as you get older.

» Long-term care insurance is for _____ homes, assisted living facilities or in-home care. _16_

» A good long-term care policy will include _____-_____ care. _17_

» You should not buy long-term care insurance until age _____. The probability of a nursing home stay _18_ before age 60 is almost zero.

» At least _____% of people over the age of 65 will require _19_ long-term care at some point.

» Long-term care insurance is *not* the same as disability or short-term medical care.

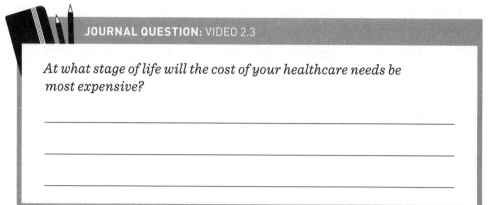

JOURNAL QUESTION: VIDEO 2.3

At what stage of life will the cost of your healthcare needs be most expensive?

_____

_____

_____

REAL LIFE
Some companies will do anything to make a buck—including insurance companies. Here are a few bizarre examples of actual insurance plans available:

- Alien abduction insurance
- Pet insurance
- Wedding insurance

VIDEO 2.4

Disability Insurance

Disability insurance is designed to replace _____ lost due to a short-term or permanent disability. It basically provides an income for you if you have an accident or health condition that prevents you from working. Once you are working full time to support yourself, you will need to have disability coverage.

» Try to buy disability insurance that pays if you cannot perform the job that you were _____ or educated to do.

» That is called _____ or "own occ" disability. Many times, this is only available for two years.

» Beware of _____-_____ policies covering less than five years. Short-term disability should be covered by your emergency fund, staying out of debt, and having a money plan.

» Disability insurance is most affordable if it is offered through your employer.

» Your coverage should be for _____% of your current income.

» The _____ period is the time between the disabling event and when the payments actually begin. A _____ elimination period will _____ your premium cost.

Identity Theft Protection

The fastest growing white-collar crime in North America today is identity theft. Identity theft happens when someone gains unauthorized access to your personal information.

According to identityhawk.com, young adults ages 18 to 24 are at the highest risk. It takes people in this age range 132 days on average to notice fraudulent activity on their accounts.

» Don't buy identity theft protection that only provides credit report _____. Credit report monitoring is something you can, and should, do yourself.

» Good protection includes _____ services that assign a _____ to clean up the mess. This means someone else will spend the time it takes to clean up the mess so you won't have to.

Remember, insurance is all about transferring risk. In this case, you're paying someone to take on the risk of cleaning up the aftermath of your stolen identity. This is someone who is ready, willing and able to go to battle with banks and creditors that will come after you to collect the debts that the thief created in your name.

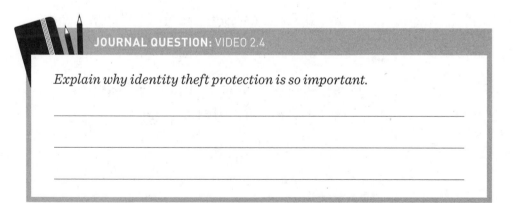

JOURNAL QUESTION: VIDEO 2.4

Explain why identity theft protection is so important.

_____

_____

_____

DO I HAVE TO PROVIDE MY SOCIAL SECURITY NUMBER TO ANY BUSINESS OR GOVERNMENT AGENCY THAT ASKS?

Go to **foundationsU.com/sshelp** to find out when it's necessary and when it's not!

- 38% of ID theft victims had a debit or credit card number stolen.
- 43% of all ID theft is a result of stolen wallets and paperwork.
- About 11% of all identity theft occurs through the internet.
- 40% of victims report profound stress in their personal lives as a result of identity theft.

identityhawk.com

WHITE-COLLAR CRIME: Financially motivated, nonviolent crime

WHAT DOES IT MEAN TO BE SELF-INSURED?

If you follow the Five Foundations, you will begin investing when you finish school and begin working in your career. Then, when you are 57 years old and the kids are grown and gone, the house is paid for, you have no debt, and you have $700,000 in mutual funds, you'll become self-insured. That means when your 20-year term is up, you shouldn't need life insurance at all—because with no kids to feed, no house payment, and $700,000 in the bank, your spouse will be financially secure in the event of your death.

Section 3:
The Importance of Life Insurance

VIDEO 3.1

Life insurance provides a monetary payout to **beneficiaries** (the person or people you elect to receive money or other assets) in the event of your death. The **financial risk** associated with death is the loss of income necessary to support your family.

» Life insurance is to replace lost income due to _____.
   31

» **Two Types of Life Insurance:**

   1. _____ insurance is for a specified period, is
      32
      substantially cheaper, is easy to understand, and has no savings plan built into it. It has one job and one job only: It replaces your income when you die.

   2. _____ _____ insurance is normally for life and
      33
      is more expensive because it funds a savings plan.

» The most common insurance myth is that the need for life insurance is a _____ situation.
   34

» If you save, invest, stay out of debt, and have a solid financial plan, you will eventually become _____-
   _____.
   35

» When purchasing life insurance, you should buy only low-cost level term. **Level term** means you pay the same amount for the entire term of the policy.

JOURNAL QUESTION: VIDEO 3.1

Which type of life insurance is the better option, term or cash value? Explain your answer.

_____

_____

_____

The Purpose and Importance of Estate Planning

"I'm a teenager. Why should I care about a will now?"

DAVE'S ANSWER: Once you turn 18, you will need to create a will. The truth is you have no idea when you'll pass away. It's not pleasant to think about, but it's important to be ready. You'll have valuable items that will be left behind, and you do not want the state deciding where your money or belongings should go.

A will includes your final wishes for your family and friends, so take your responsibility seriously. You should identify people in your life who will receive these valuables, or assets. Do not rely on your state government to distribute your wealth.

✱ **NOTE:** Get more information on creating a will by completing the Chapter 9 activity "What's With the Will?"

Budget Builder

Insurance isn't exciting. But it is necessary and so appreciated when you need it! Go to foundationsU.com/9 to build insurance premiums into your budget.

Section 4 : Insurance to Avoid

VIDEO 4.1

Bad Ideas in the Insurance World

» _____ life/disability: pays off a borrower's debt if that borrower dies or becomes disabled (your term life insurance already covers this)
36

» Credit _____ protection: insures your credit card debt (you should avoid owning a credit card, period)
37

» _____ and hospital indemnity insurance: insures you against cancer or other medical issues (your health insurance already covers this)
38

» Accidental _____: insures you against unexpected accidents that cause your death (your term life insurance already covers this)
39

» Any insurance with _____ _____, investments or refunds: anything that combines insurance with investments is a bad idea
40

» Prepaid _____ policies: if invested instead, this money would pay for the burial policy many times over
41

» _____ life insurance: pays off your home mortgage if you die unexpectedly or become disabled (your term life insurance, which is 10 to 15 times cheaper, already covers this)
42

» Any kind of _____ coverage: any extra
insurance on top of your existing insurance (remember,
you only need one policy for each type of insurance); the
two insurance companies fight over who pays the bills
and nothing gets accomplished

JOURNAL QUESTION: VIDEO 4.1

What is duplicate coverage, and why should you avoid it?

_____

_____

_____

Cash Value vs. Term + Roth IRA

Cash value life insurance is a bad investment. Consider this:

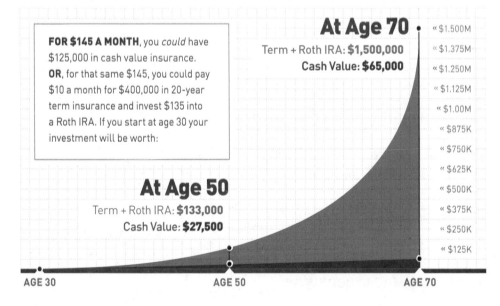

FOR $145 A MONTH, you *could* have
$125,000 in cash value insurance.
OR, for that same $145, you could pay
$10 a month for $400,000 in 20-year
term insurance and invest $135 into
a Roth IRA. If you start at age 30 your
investment will be worth:

At Age 70
Term + Roth IRA: **$1,500,000**
Cash Value: **$65,000**

At Age 50
Term + Roth IRA: **$133,000**
Cash Value: **$27,500**

« $1.500M
« $1.375M
« $1.250M
« $1.125M
« $1.00M
« $875K
« $750K
« $625K
« $500K
« $375K
« $250K
« $125K

AGE 30   AGE 50   AGE 70

Chapter Summary

 ## Check for Understanding

Now it's time to check your learning! Go back to the Before You Begin section for this chapter. Place a checkmark next to the learning outcomes you've mastered and complete the "after" column of the Measure Your Progress section.

 ## Take Action Challenge

Garret owns an older car worth about $5,000. He thinks he is paying too much for auto insurance and wants to find out how he can save money. He decides to look into raising his deductible from $250 to $1,000. By doing this, he can save $200 per year. Use the break-even analysis (found in Section 2): If Garret raises the deductible, will it be worth the risk? Defend your answer.

_____

_____

_____

 ## Big Ideas

The following Big Ideas are intended to provide clear focus and purpose to the lessons. Read each statement and think about how what you've learned will affect your current and future decisions. Then, in the space provided, write an "I believe" statement for each of the Big Ideas.

» Managing risk is a major part of a healthy financial plan.

_____

» The purpose of insurance is to transfer risk.

_____

» Insurance is a product—be a wise consumer!

_____

 # Build On What You've Learned

Complete the graphic organizer below.

TYPE OF INSURANCE NEEDED	FINANCIAL RISK COVERED	STAGE OF LIFE NEEDED
1. Homeowner's or Renter's		
2.	Cost of damage to your vehicle, liability and medical in the event of an accident or other event that may damage your vehicle	
3. Health		You should always have health insurance.
4.	Your income in the case of illness or injury that prevents you from working	
5.		At age 60 and above
6. Identity Theft Protection	The cost of hiring someone who has the time and knowledge to clean up the mess	
7.		When you have dependants who rely on your income until you become self-insured

Money in Review

Matching

Match the following terms to the correct definition below.

> Ⓐ Deductible   Ⓓ Premium   Ⓖ Out-of-Pocket Expense
>
> Ⓑ Policy   Ⓔ Liability
>
> Ⓒ Claim   Ⓕ Coverage

1. _____ Specific amount of money that you pay when insurance only covers a portion of costs

2. _____ Paperwork filed with an insurance company in order to get them to cover a loss for someone they insure

3. _____ Describes the type of coverage in an insurance agreement

4. _____ Amount you pay monthly, quarterly, semiannually or annually to purchase different types of insurance

5. _____ Applies to the amount of protection you have through an insurance company in the event of a loss

6. _____ Amount you must pay before you begin receiving any benefits from your insurance company

7. _____ The state or quality of being obligated according to law or equity

Illustration

Draw a picture representation of each of the following terms.

> **Financial Risk**
>

> **Insurance**
>

Multiple Choice

Circle the correct answer.

8. Raising your deductible may be a good option when it comes to lowering your premium, but it is important to do a break-even analysis before making that decision.

   Ⓐ True
   Ⓑ False

9. Financially, it makes sense to stay on your parents' auto insurance policy through college if possible.

   Ⓐ True
   Ⓑ False

10. Which of the following would *not* be a huge financial risk (and, therefore would not require insurance) if you had a full emergency fund of $500 or more?

    Ⓐ A car accident
    Ⓑ A lost cell phone
    Ⓒ A medical emergency
    Ⓓ Stolen identity

11. The time between the disabling event and the beginning of payments in your disability coverage is called:

    Ⓐ Deductible
    Ⓑ Out of pocket
    Ⓒ Stop gap
    Ⓓ Elimination period

12. A life insurance policy that covers a specific period of time is called:

    Ⓐ Whole life
    Ⓑ Term
    Ⓒ Universal
    Ⓓ Level

Short Answer

Respond in the space provided.

13. What does it mean to "transfer risk"?

    _____
    _____
    _____

14. Explain the importance of liability protection.

    _____
    _____
    _____

15. Why should life insurance not be used as an investment?

    _____
    _____
    _____

16. Explain how someone becomes self-insured.

    _____
    _____
    _____

17. What are some unnecessary types of insurance? Why are these unnecessary?

    _____
    _____
    _____

What do other high school students know about money and relationships?

We asked high school students if they've ever witnessed money affecting a relationship close to them.

....

"Money is always a strain at my house. At least every other day, my parents fight about money."

Junior, Michigan

"When my parents fight, it is usually concerning a large purchase that they didn't discuss."

Senior, Wyoming

"My parents fought all the time about money and are now divorcing."

Senior, Alabama

"Money was the cause of my parents' divorce when I was 5 years old."

Senior, Oklahoma

"I argue with my parents all the time about money. I don't understand why they say no to giving me the spending money I ask for, even though we seem to be fine financially."

Junior, Florida

Money and Relationships

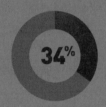

34%

of teens receive a weekly allowance of, on average, just over $16 per week.*

28%

of teens are borrowing money. On average they owe $252. They most frequently owe money to their parents, school or friends.*

MONEY AND RELATIONSHIPS go hand in hand, which means the way you handle your money affects everyone around you. Hard to imagine, right? Well it's true. Whether you save, overspend, are generous in your giving, or often borrow from friends—people notice. Your current and future relationships will all be influenced by how you handle money. So let's make it a priority now to learn more about this topic.

*Charles Schwab Teens & Money Survey (2011)

Before You Begin

 Learning Outcomes

Once you've completed this chapter's videos, you will be asked to return to this list of learning outcomes and place a checkmark next to the items you've mastered.

Section 1: Understanding Your Money Personality

☐ Identify differences among people's values and attitudes as they relate to money.

☐ Evaluate your own money personality.

Section 2: Marriage and Money

☐ Evaluate how discussing important financial matters with household members can reduce conflict.

☐ Understand how having a budget or a money plan can reduce conflict.

Section 3: Communication Is Key

☐ Understand the value of discussing individual and shared financial responsibilities.

☐ Develop communication strategies for discussing financial issues.

☐ Integrate healthy communication about money with parents, friends and others.

 Key Terms

Get to know the language of money.

» **Accountability:** The quality or state of being responsible, liable or answerable

» **Free Spirit:** A person who thinks that everything will work out fine and typically hates to deal with the details

» **Nerd:** A person who is picky about budgeting and details

» **Time poverty:** A situation in which a person is lacking time, which leads to stress

» **Value system:** A person's priorities, beliefs and standards that affect how he or she views the world

Measure Your Progress

Before you watch the Money and Relationships video, take the following survey to see if you have more Free Spirit or Nerd tendencies. Check the characteristics that best describe you.

FREE SPIRITS tend to be:	NERDS tend to be:
☐ Creative	☐ Number-oriented (enjoy working with numbers)
☐ Spontaneous	☐ Rule followers
☐ Less organized and not concerned about rules	☐ Organized
☐ Late for meetings, dates, appointments—most everything	☐ On time for everything
☐ Easygoing	☐ Slow and steady when making decisions

JOURNAL QUESTION: INTRODUCTION

What are your initial thoughts about money and relationships? What do you want to learn about money and relationships?

_____

_____

_____

CHAPTER 10

Information not otherwise sourced in this section is based on Dave Ramsey's personal experience counseling families for more than 20 years.

"Your priorities, passions, goals and fears are shown clearly in the flow of your money."

DAVE RAMSEY

Section 1:
Understanding Your Money Personality

VIDEO 1.1

Values and Attitudes

HOW DO YOUR VALUES RELATE TO MONEY? If you value security, you are more likely to be a saver. If you value freedom and spontaneity, you're probably more likely to spend. When handling money, it's difficult to balance who you are with what you should do. Being aware of your money personality will help you create a plan to accommodate both. When it comes to relating with others about money, it's important to also consider their values.

Men, Women and Money (Over-Generalizing)

Men and women generally approach money in very different ways. Of course, not all men and women will relate to money in this way, but there are some patterns that have proved themselves over and over again.

The flow of money in a family represents the _____ _____ under which that family operates. Where your money goes is an indication of what is important to you.

Emergency Fund Savings

» Men: "It's boring and not _____ enough."

» Women: "It's the most _____ key to our financial plan."

Shopping

» Men get good deals by _____. They want to win.

» Women get good deals by _____. They enjoy the process.

Financial Problems

» Men lose _____-_____ when money problems pop up, because money usually represents a scorecard to them.

» Women experience _____ or even _____ when money problems arise. With women, money usually represents _____.

> "Personal relationships are the fertile soil from which all advancement, all success, all achievement in real life grows."
>
> **BEN STEIN**
> American actor, writer and commentator

More teen girls than boys report saving their money for small purchases like music or clothes. (27% boys, 36% girls)

More teen boys than girls report saving their money for bigger purchases, like a car. (48% boys, 37% girls)

Charles Schwab Teens & Money Survey (2011)

JOURNAL QUESTION: VIDEO 1.1

Have you ever witnessed money affecting a relationship close to you?

_____

_____

_____

Section 2: Marriage and Money

VIDEO 2.1

It takes teamwork! If men and women are so different, who is supposed to do the financial decision making in a marriage? BOTH! Handling money is the responsibility of both people in a relationship. Although one person might have a natural gift for budgeting and working with numbers, the decision making has to be done together. Communication, teamwork and consistency are all important elements of handling family finances.

» The number-one cause of divorce in America is money _____. If it's the number-one problem, that means it is also the number-one opportunity to improve a marriage.

» When you agree on your spending, that means that you also agree on your value system.

» The _____ likes doing the budget because it gives them control, and they feel like they are taking care of loved ones.

» The _____ _____ feels controlled, not cared for, and can appear irresponsible to the Nerd.

In a marriage, you are financially accountable to one another. That's why having a monthly budget is so important. Not only does it tell your money what to do, but it also represents two people agreeing on what they want their money to do.

JOURNAL QUESTION: VIDEO 2.1

Would you describe yourself as a Nerd or a Free Spirit when it comes to handling money? Explain your answer.

_____

_____

_____

Will My Boyfriend's Credit Score Affect Me?

"My boyfriend's credit is in bad shape, and we're thinking about getting married someday. Will his bad credit rating affect mine? My credit is in good shape right now."

DAVE'S ANSWER: Marrying someone with a bad credit rating will not affect your score. In other words, the black marks on his credit rating don't jump across the aisle onto your report as soon as he slips the ring on your finger.

After you're married, your husband will be listed as "spouse" on your report. Then, if they pull your report for any reason, they'll see that half of your "team" has had some problems in the past. When the two of you decide to buy a home, it may be difficult if there are still problems with his credit report.

But the big issue here is that you seem to have differing views on money management. Make sure you go through premarital counseling together and begin the process of working together to make monthly budgets. If you get married, money is going to be a big part of your lives for a long time. Agreeing on your goals now will set the foundation for your dreams.

Section 3: Communication Is Key

`VIDEO 3.1`

The Budget Committee Meeting

» The budget committee meeting is a great way to learn how to communicate and avoid conflict when it comes to money and marriage.

» The Nerd should be the one to prepare the budget, but the decision making must be done by both people.

» Remember the basics of budgeting: You spend every dollar on paper before the month begins. Every dollar has a name or a purpose.

According to a recent Charles Schwab Teens & Money Survey (2011), 9 out of 10 teens say they were "affected by the recession," causing major shifts in perspective that include a greater appreciation for what they have and an increased awareness of financial hardship.

How to Talk to Your Parents About Money

Some of you have parents who pay for everything. Others have parents who won't give you a dime—if you want something, even if it's important, it's your responsibility. The rest of you may have parents who fall somewhere in the middle.

You can't control your parents, but what you can do is _____ to them. If you want to learn how to manage money before taking on the bills and responsibilities of an adult, you need to be in open communication with your parents.

Talk about your _____. Share your thoughts on money, what you want to start paying for, and the things you may need help paying for.

_____ your parents' decisions. Don't beg or manipulate. The goal here isn't to get more money out of your parents. Instead, it's to become responsible and independent with the money you have.

Singles and Money

It won't be long before you're an adult managing your own money and paying your own bills. You'll find that managing your money alone creates some unique challenges. You go from being accountable to your parents to making all your choices on your own, which can make it easy to get off track when it comes to your financial goals. Single adults need to be proactive about having financial accountability in their lives.

» _____ _____ and fatigue can lead to poor money management. Young singles who are in college or just getting started in their career typically pour all of their time and energy into that. It's easy to let your

PRACTICAL TIPS FOR COMMUNICATING WITH OTHERS ABOUT MONEY

1. **Listen.** Communicating with others isn't just about expressing your own wants and needs—it's also about listening to what others want and need.

2. **Pick the right time and place.** Starting a conversation with your mom or dad two minutes before they need to leave for work is not ideal. Make sure there is time for both of you to have a relaxed and complete conversation.

3. **Be honest.** When it comes to money and relationships, honesty is key.

4. **Seek counsel.** You're young, and there will be money mistakes in your future. One of the best ways to avoid these mistakes is to seek advice from trusted adults—even if it's not the answer you want to hear.

5. **Communicate your money goals.** Let your parents and others close to you know about your goals. Doing this will help provide accountability and encouragement along the way.

busy life keep you from reconciling your account, much less writing a budget each month. If you let this happen, financially you'll end up just treading water and not going anywhere. Even with a tight schedule, managing your money must remain a priority.

» Beware of _____ buying, which can be brought on by _____ or even by the "I owe it to myself" syndrome. With no one's opinion or input to worry about, single adults can rationalize almost any expense. If you're single, you have a greater responsibility to manage your money because no one is looking over your shoulder. It's up to you!

» A written plan gives the single person empowerment, self-accountability and _____. You must do a budget every month! A written plan gives you peace of mind and keeps you on track to reach your goals.

» Develop an _____ relationship. This is someone with whom you discuss major _____ and your budget. Accountability friends must love you enough to be brutally honest and promise to do so for your own good.

Budget Builder

Is your money personality and value system evident in your budget? Go to foundationsU.com/10 for your next budget lesson.

"When you learn to respect others, you will see yourself improve in self-esteem, happiness and fulfillment."

SHARON RAMSEY

MONEY TOPICS TEENS WOULD LIKE TO TALK ABOUT WITH THEIR PARENTS

1. How to invest money

2. Their career aspirations

3. How to budget money

Charles Schwab Teens & Money Survey (2011)

JOURNAL QUESTION: VIDEO 3.1

How will this chapter change the way you talk to your parents about money?

_____

_____

_____

Chapter Summary

 Check for Understanding

Now it's time to check your learning! Go back to the Before You Begin section for this chapter and place a checkmark next to the learning outcomes you've mastered. Review the Measure Your Progress section to see if any of your answers have changed.

 **Big Ideas**

The following Big Ideas are intended to provide clear focus and purpose to the lessons. Read each statement and think about how what you've learned will affect your current and future decisions. Then, in the space provided, write an "I believe" statement for each of the Big Ideas.

» How you handle money will affect your relationships.

_____

» Know your money personality.

_____

» Communication is key!

_____

Build On What You've Learned

Draw a picture of yourself in the space below (a stick figure will work fine). Label your drawing with elements of your money personality and values. Compare your drawing with your peers'. In what ways are your money personalities and values similar? In what ways are they different?

⚡ Take Action Challenge

Reflect on your self-portrait. Think about your money personality and values. Now consider your spending and saving habits. In the space below, write about how your money personality and values relate to how you handle your money.

_____

_____

_____

_____

Money in Review

Matching

Match the following terms to the correct definition below.

> **A** Nerd   **C** Time Poverty   **E** Accountability
>
> **B** Value System   **D** Free Spirit

1. _____ A person who is picky about budgeting and details

2. _____ The quality or state of being responsible, liable or answerable

3. _____ A situation in which a person is lacking time, which leads to stress

4. _____ A person who thinks that everything will work out fine and typically hates to deal with the details

5. _____ A person's priorities, beliefs and standards that affect how he or she views the world

Illustration

Draw a picture representation of each of the following terms.

Conflict	Respect

Multiple Choice
Circle the correct answer.

6. Communicating about financial issues and goals in a relationship can reduce conflict.
   - Ⓐ True
   - Ⓑ False

7. When it comes to managing money, your personality and values have no importance.
   - Ⓐ True
   - Ⓑ False

8. Which of the following present challenges to managing money as a single adult?
   - Ⓐ Time poverty
   - Ⓑ Being accountable to no one
   - Ⓒ Impulse buys
   - Ⓓ All of the above

9. When it comes to communicating with others about money, you should not:
   - Ⓐ Listen
   - Ⓑ Manipulate
   - Ⓒ Pick the right time and place
   - Ⓓ Be honest

10. When married couples do not share goals and values in how they manage money, which of the following can occur?
    - Ⓐ Conflict
    - Ⓑ Divorce
    - Ⓒ Stress
    - Ⓓ All of the above

Short Answer
Respond in the space provided.

11. Describe some general differences in how men and women relate with money.

    _____

    _____

    _____

12. How does communication about important financial matters in households reduce conflict?

    _____

    _____

    _____

13. How does having a budget reduce conflict in relationships?

    _____

    _____

    _____

14. Summarize challenges you'll face managing money as a young single adult.

    _____

    _____

    _____

15. Summarize ways that you can overcome the challenges you listed in question 14.

    _____

    _____

    _____

CHAPTER 11

What do other high school students know about taxes?

We asked other high school students how they think taxes will affect them.

....

"Many people struggle with understanding how they work (like me)."

Junior, Louisiana

"We all have to pay them, and sometimes we get taxes back."

Sophomore, Texas

"They are taken out of every paycheck."

Senior, Minnesota

"You pay taxes on everything you own, but then they give you a tax return or something like that."

Junior, Illinois

Careers and Taxes

35%

of teens do not know anyone who works at their dream job.[*]

66%

of teens said their chosen career will require four or more years of college.[*]

IT MIGHT SEEM overwhelming to consider all the career opportunities in the world today and have to land on just one. But now is an important time to start selecting, preparing and planning for your future career. Obviously, income is important. But when it comes to careers, it's not just about money. The goal of your professional life should be to devote yourself to your passion and calling, finding somewhere and some way to make a living by working in your strengths.

[*]Junior Achievement Teens and Careers Survey 2012

Before You Begin

Learning Outcomes

Once you've completed this chapter's videos, you will be asked to return to this list of learning outcomes and place a checkmark next to the items you've mastered.

Section 1: Self-Assessment

☐ Identify your personal strengths and weaknesses.

Section 2: Goal Setting

☐ Clarify your educational and career goals.

☐ Understand the components of goal setting.

Section 3: You Won't Love the Entry Level

☐ Understand the value of entry-level jobs.

☐ Identify valuable work attributes outside of your general skill set.

Section 4: Best Practices of Successful People

☐ Identify the best practices of successful people.

☐ Develop a résumé.

☐ Analyze the interview process and develop personal interview skills.

Section 5: Income and Taxes

☐ Describe factors affecting take-home pay.

☐ Identify sources of personal income.

☐ Identify different types of taxes.

☐ Be familiar with various documents for reporting taxes.

☐ Analyze the costs and benefits of paying taxes and the cost of government services.

Key Terms

Get to know the language of money.

» **Earned income:** Any income (wages/salary) that is generated by working

» **Income tax:** Tax paid out by anyone who earns an income

» **Passive income:** Money earned on a regular basis with little or no effort required to maintain it. Some things that produce passive income are real estate, intellectual property like books or internet content, or a business in which the owner is not actively involved.

» **Personal branding:** The process by which we "market" ourselves to others; involves highlighting personal strengths, interests and unique qualities and identifying goals

» **Portfolio income:** Income generated by selling an investment at a higher price than you paid for it

» **Property taxes:** Taxes paid by anyone who owns property such as land, a home or commercial real estate

» **Résumé:** A brief account of one's professional or work experience and qualifications, often submitted with an employment application

» **Sales tax:** Tax on goods and services that goes to your state or local government

» **Social Security:** A federal insurance program funded by taxpayer dollars that provides benefits to people who are retired, unemployed or disabled

Measure Your Progress

The majority of this chapter is about choosing a career that blends your strengths, interests, abilities and personality traits. Whether you are going to college or straight into the workforce, you will need to be able to answer some basic questions about yourself. The answers to these questions will not only help guide you in your career path, but they will prepare you for interviews as well. Take some time to answer these questions:

JOURNAL QUESTION: INTRODUCTION

1. What are your interests?

_____

_____

2. What are your career goals?

_____

_____

3. How would you describe yourself?

_____

_____

4. Describe your ability to work as part of a team.

_____

_____

> *"The mindset today is you have to know who you are and how you function in the market. That's the only security you have."*
>
> DAVE RAMSEY

- 43% of teens are "very confident" they will someday have their dream job.

- 71% of teens would consider giving up their dream job for one that paid a higher salary.

Junior Achievement Teens and Careers Survey 2012

11 CHAPTER

Section 1: Self-Assessment

VIDEO 1.1

A Message From Dave

THE JOB MARKET is changing, so you must be prepared to change with it. My grandfather was an incredible man. He was one of my heroes, actually. He entered the workforce during one of the most difficult periods in American history, the Great Depression. Life wasn't easy back then, but he enjoyed his work, loved his family, and poured himself into both. He started in the accounting department at Alcoa, an aluminum company, as a very young man, and over time he grew into one of their head cost accountants. Grandpa stayed with Alcoa for 38 years, until the day he retired from the workforce. He left with a gold watch and a pension, as well as the satisfaction of knowing he'd devoted his entire working life to a single company. Those days are gone in America. Companies, products, services, startups and shutdowns are moving faster today than ever before. The rate of change going on in the workplace is mind-blowing! My grandfather, God love him, would be completely out of place in today's market. Throughout this course, we focus almost entirely on the "outgo." That is, we budget and plan how to spend and save our money. That's what the Five Foundations are all about, right? It's how we tell our money what to do once it leaves our hands. In this chapter we switch gears and examine your income.

Consider This When Choosing a Career Path

» Deciding on a career is not as hard as you think.
Ask yourself: What do you love to do? What are you
_____ good at? What hobbies and interests
do you already have that you could turn into a career?

» You can experiment by getting a part-time job,
volunteering, or just _____ someone on a job you
are interested in. While you are there, ask questions!

» Invest time in _____ your decision rather than
spending time _____ it later.

» Remember, just because a particular job pays well
doesn't mean it will be something you _____.

» Don't get money and happiness _____!

» The job market constantly changes—and so do _____.
Even if you decide the career you chose doesn't fit you
10 years from now, it's not the end of the world. It's
actually _____.

» What's most important is that you do what you love;
do what you're naturally good at. If you do that with
_____, you won't have to worry about money.

Identify Your Personal Strengths and Weaknesses

The average worker today will have 10 different jobs by age 40 and could have as many as 20 different jobs during his or her working lifetime. Unlike past generations of Americans, the modern workforce finds security not in the longevity of their employment with a single, stable company, but rather in understanding who they are and what they want to be doing. The focus has shifted away from the big corporations and toward the individual's strengths and passions.

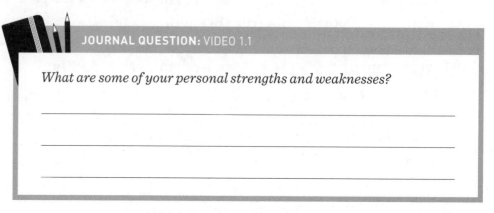

JOURNAL QUESTION: VIDEO 1.1

What are some of your personal strengths and weaknesses?

_____

_____

_____

VIDEO 1.2

A Message From Jon
How to Stay Positive

Everyone has them: those nagging voices of fear and doubt. They only get loud when you do things that matter. And since you're going to do a lot of things that matter, you can expect some voices headed your way. So what can you do? You're going to beat your voices by doing three things:

1. _____ **them down.** Voices are invisible bullies, and they hate when you make them visible. The best way to do that is to write them down in a simple notebook. They can't stand to be documented, because the minute they are, you can see how stupid they are. Lies hate the light of day.

---

2. _____ **them with truth.** Never argue with a voice. That's a never-ending tangled discussion you won't escape from any time soon.

3. _____ **your voices.** Do you know what fear and doubt fear? Community. One of fear and doubt's chief aims is to make you feel alone—like you're the only one who feels a certain way. Fear wants to isolate you. As long as you keep your fear to yourself, no one can tell you the truth about it.

Build Your Brand

Most people know what a brand is. Who makes your favorite shoes or soft drink? But do you know why branding is important when selling a product? Companies spend a lot of money on developing their specific brand message. A brand is meant to tell the "story" of a product through creative packaging and advertising in order to distinguish it from the competition.

Personal branding has the same purpose. It's simply a process of identifying your skills, experiences and strengths and marketing those in the most effective way. You want to leverage your education and personal attributes for success. For example, say you spend a semester of college studying Spanish in a third-world country. You would want to be intentional about how you market that unique experience on your résumé. What you learned and how you grew as an individual were just as important as the skill of speaking a foreign language.

JOURNAL QUESTION: VIDEO 1.2

Write down what your negative voice says about you. Refute that voice with the truth and share it with others.

_____

_____

_____

VIDEO 1.3: THERE ARE NO FILL-INS FOR THIS SECTION

Just Because You're Good at Something Doesn't Make It a Strength

According to Marcus Buckingham, author of *Go Put Your Strengths To Work*, "most people think your strengths are what you're good at, and your weaknesses are what you're bad at." He explains that this isn't a good way to measure your strengths and weaknesses. There may be a lot of things that you're good at but hate doing. Just because you're good at something doesn't make it a strength. You also must have a passion for what you're doing—that's what qualifies it as a strength. "A better definition of a strength," says Buckingham, "is an activity that makes you feel strong. And a weakness is an activity that makes you feel weak. Even if you're good at it, if it drains you, that's a weakness."

You Never Outgrow Who You Are

Even though your knowledge and work experience will change throughout your life, you'll never outgrow who you are. Everyone has natural tendencies, strengths and weaknesses that are intertwined with who they are as people. You cannot leave it up to someone else to tell you what you should do with your life—not your parents, your friends or your teachers. Your career must engage your strengths, not silence them. For example, if you have high energy and love interacting with others, then a job that requires you to sit at a desk all day where you are isolated from others probably would not be a good fit for you.

JOURNAL QUESTION: VIDEO 1.3

Which careers compliment your passions and strengths?

_____

_____

_____

The DISC is a popular system originally based on the work of an American psychologist named William Moulton Marston in the 1920s.

TEST YOURSELF

Go to foundationsU.com and take the DISC Personality Profile.

"The way to succeed is to identify your strengths and weaknesses, then seek goals that fit those strengths and weaknesses using tactics and strategies that take advantage of your strengths and sidestep your weaknesses."

JOHN T. REED
American businessman, author and investor

DISC Personality Profile

Understanding your own strengths and weaknesses should be a top priority. Remember, people who only work for money are miserable because there is no fulfillment or meaning in their careers. You must find something that blends your skills, abilities, personality traits, values, dreams and passions.

D

I

Persuader

Conductor

Promoter

FAST

10% POPULATION

Decisive

CHARACTERISTICS
Driver; Results-oriented;
Overlooks details; Focuses on the
bottom line; Can hurt feelings

CONCERNED WITH
When

ANIMAL
Lion

25% POPULATION

Interactive

CHARACTERISTICS
Expressive; Can lose focus;
Persuasive; Good at speaking;
Likes entertaining; Impulsive

CONCERNED WITH
Who

ANIMAL
Otter

Implementor

Relator

TASKS ← → PEOPLE

25% POPULATION

Cautious

CHARACTERISTICS
Detail-oriented; Can seem rigid;
Analytical; Resistant to change;
Logical; Can be too serious

CONCERNED WITH
How

ANIMAL
Beaver

40% POPULATION

Stabilizing

CHARACTERISTICS
Loyal; Dislikes conflict; Amiable;
Calm; Can seem unenthusiastic;
Understanding; Team player

CONCERNED WITH
Why

ANIMAL
Golden Retriever

Analyzer

Supporter

SLOW

C

S

Coordinator

📊 What Kind of Job Do You Want After Graduation?

Take a look at the graph below to see what fields of employment teens are most interested in.

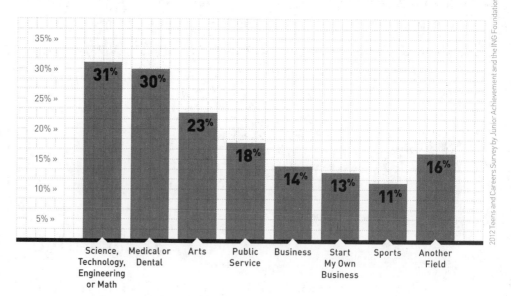

- Science, Technology, Engineering or Math: 31%
- Medical or Dental: 30%
- Arts: 23%
- Public Service: 18%
- Business: 14%
- Start My Own Business: 13%
- Sports: 11%
- Another Field: 16%

2012 Teens and Careers Survey by Junior Achievement and the ING Foundation

SET YOUR GOALS!

In which areas of life do you most need to set goals? Go to **foundationsU.com/wheel** to take Zig Ziglar's Wheel of Life Quiz.

"What causes you to hit goals is not the things you're willing to do to accomplish them. It's the things you're willing to sacrifice."

DAVE RAMSEY

Section 2: Goal Setting

VIDEO 2.1

Goal-Setting Categories

It is important to have a goal for each area of your life.

- » Career
- » Education
- » Financial
- » Family
- » Spiritual
- » Social
- » Physical

Goal Guidelines

How do you take a goal from fuzzy and undefined to crystal clear and actionable? Your goals must:

» **Be _____.** How will you know you've achieved your goal? Give yourself a time limit and some other measure of achievement.

» **Be _____.** Don't just say, "I am going to save for a car." Have a specific car and a specific price in mind.

» **Have _____ _____.** If your goal has no end in sight, you'll get discouraged. Plan to accomplish your goals by a specific date.

» **Be _____ goals.** Example: If you want to be a doctor and, therefore, you go to medical school, great! If your parents want you to be a doctor and, therefore, you go to medical school, I don't want to be your patient! You may accomplish a goal that someone else has set for you, but you won't be passionate about it.

» **Be _____ down.** Writing your goals down gives you clarity and focus. A written goal is also a powerful reminder that you can use to keep you on track.

OTHER IMPORTANT ELEMENTS OF GOAL SETTING

- **Make sure you have some accountability.** Share your goals with the people closest to you. Give them an opportunity to encourage you along the way.

- **Eliminate distractions.** It's important not to let yourself get sidetracked.

- **Write goals in the positive, not the negative.** Focus on what you're going to achieve, not what you're going to give up.

- **Read your goals on a regular basis.** Post them where you can see them.

- **Make your goals challenging, but attainable.** For long-term goals, try breaking them into smaller steps.

Is walking from fuzzy goal to real action easy to do? Not always. But the clearer your goals are, the more likely you are to actually reach them.

Ready to be an effective goal setter? Go to **foundationsU.com/goals** to use our Goal Tracker tool.

JOURNAL QUESTION: VIDEO 2.1

Describe a recent goal you set for yourself. What did you do to make reaching that goal a success?

_____

_____

_____

Section 3:
You Won't Love the Entry Level

`VIDEO 3.1`

What Will Life Be Like When You Move Out?

Maybe you're assuming that when you're on your own, you'll have as big of a house and as nice of a car and take the same kind of vacations as your parents. And you aren't alone; 59% of your peers believe they will do even BETTER financially than their parents. But here's the deal: Your parents didn't have those things when they were starting out. Just ask them what life was like when they were starting out. Listen to the story of their humble beginnings—their first apartment or car or where they went out to eat for dinner.

The truth is—having the same lifestyle as your parents won't be automatic or immediate.

» Average rent on a one-bedroom apartment in most cities is about $_____$ a month! Water and electricity—which are kind of important—we're talking $200 a month. Food will cost you about $250 a month—and yes, that's for just one person. That's $1,200 a month already!

» College graduates who actually get a job in their field out of college might start out with $35,000 to $45,000 a year. But if you factor in the graduates who are unemployed or underemployed because they can't find work in their career field, the average salary drops to around $_____.

» Don't expect to see all of that $27,000 come home with you. That's because _____ will eat up 20 to 25% of your paycheck.

» That only leaves you about $600 a month for things like transportation, clothes, cable and a cell phone—not to mention saving, _____ and having fun with your friends. [21]

» You might think having a full-time job means you'll be able to go out and buy whatever you want. But that's just not real life. That's why it's crucial to know how to _____ now! [22]

Someday you'll think back to your first car with one working window or your thrift-store coffee table and you'll laugh—because they were pieces of junk, sure, but also because those little sacrifices paved the way for a great future.

It takes time and being smart with your money to build wealth. So get an education, budget your income, save for big items, and invest early for your future. As you move up in your career, your income will grow—and if you do what we teach, you will win with money.

Overtime and Extra Jobs

Many people work extra jobs or overtime in order to pay off debt. If you have debt, attack it now by picking up extra work opportunities. Once you are out of debt, or if you are wise and avoid debt altogether, these jobs will be a thing of the past.

"Choose a job you love, and you will never have to work a day in your life."

CONFUCIUS
Chinese teacher, politician and philosopher

JOURNAL QUESTION: VIDEO 3.1

Describe a work experience that has helped you develop valuable career attributes such as a strong work ethic, respect, commitment, etc.

_____

_____

_____

Section 4:
Best Practices of Successful People

VIDEO 4.1: THERE ARE NO FILL-INS FOR THIS SECTION

Take notes in the spaces provided.

Five Things Successful People Always Do

1. They start. _____

2. They fight fear. _____

3. They ignore haters. _____

4. They stay humble and hungry. _____

5. They give to others. _____

A Message From Dave on Contentment

Over the years, I've been able to talk to a lot of men and women at all different income levels and at all different levels of wealth. I've met people making $150,000 who are flat broke and up to their eyeballs in debt, and I've met people making $50,000 who are debt-free, building wealth, and winning with money. How's that possible? How can someone be winning at $50,000 while someone else is losing—big time—at $150,000? The answer may surprise you. I think this one thing is so fundamental that it's impossible to be successful without it. I'm talking about contentment.

Five Lands on the Road to Awesome

1. Learning _____

2. Editing _____

3. Mastering _____

4. Harvesting _____

5. Guiding _____

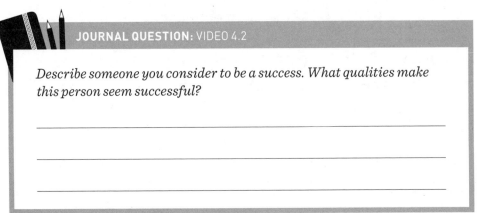

JOURNAL QUESTION: VIDEO 4.1

Look back at Jon's list of "Five Things Successful People Always Do." Which of these comes naturally to you? Which of these do you struggle with?

_____

_____

_____

VIDEO 4.2: THERE ARE NO FILL-INS FOR THIS SECTION

A Story About Mentorship

> **"** *I was lucky to have the right heroes. Tell me who your heroes are and I'll tell you how you'll turn out to be. The qualities of the one you admire are the traits that you, with a little practice, can make your own, and that, if practiced, will become habit forming.*"

WARREN BUFFETT, Legendary investor

Warren Buffett, billionaire and chairman of Berkshire Hathaway, knows the value of a mentor. Buffett's father, a stockbroker, was his first mentor. He guided young Warren as he spread his business and investing wings at an early age.

Buffett's next mentor was Ben Graham, author of *The Intelligent Investor*, and Buffett's professor at Columbia University. Following in the footsteps of these "heroes," Buffett became one of the wealthiest men in the world, eventually mentoring another one of the wealthiest men in the world, Bill Gates.

Whatever your goals in life, if you desire success, find a person who has achieved success and follow in their footsteps.

JOURNAL QUESTION: VIDEO 4.2

Describe someone you consider to be a success. What qualities make this person seem successful?

_____

_____

_____

KEYS TO MAKING MENTORSHIP A REAL BENEFIT

- **Choose wisely.** The goal of this relationship is to improve your habits and values as you work toward your goals. Often, your mentor will be older than you and in the next stage of life, so you can gain from their experiences.

- **Take action.** If all you do is meet with your mentor, you're not going to get much from the relationship. Even the best mentoring relationship is a failure if you don't follow through and act on what you've learned.

- **Change it up.** You may find that you need different mentors as you progress through different stages of life.

One last thought:
Mentoring is a cycle. Keep it going and return the favor of all the wisdom you received from your mentor by being willing to become a mentor yourself someday.

"As iron sharpens iron, so one person sharpens another."

Proverbs 27:17

VIDEO 4.3

Job Search and Résumé Basics

Job Hunting

» Companies do not start out looking for _____.
They have a specific _____, and they need someone
to meet it.

» Develop a strategy: Identify your _____ job/employer
and _____ everything you can about them.

Applying for a Job

When it is time to contact the company, think of it like starting a new relationship with a person. After you target the companies where you would most like to work, you are going to contact them at least three times.

1. **Introduction _____:** The primary purpose of an introduction letter is to introduce yourself to a company. This is usually your first point of contact with a business.

2. **Cover letter and résumé:** Your cover letter should be specific to the position you are applying for, relating your experience, skills and experience to the position for which you are applying. Your résumé should present your background and skills to an employer.

3. **Phone follow-up:** Make sure your initial introduction letter and résumé are followed with more personal contact with the employer.

Interviews and jobs come from persistent follow-up and _____.

TO FIND A JOB, EXPAND THREE CIRCLES

1. **Geography:** Be willing to work a greater distance from home or move to another city if necessary.

2. **Industry:** Don't get caught up looking for a specific job title. Be willing to look at related career fields.

3. **Permanence:** If a full-time position is not available, be willing to work part time or as a temporary employee.

Small circles will limit you, e.g., "I only want to work in advertising in a full-time position in Nashville."

Expand the circles, e.g., "I will work anywhere in the Southeast, in advertising, marketing or corporate communications and will take part-time contract work."

Your résumé should include a *Results* paragraph at the top. This is just one or two lines that highlight something important you've accomplished. In high school, your key results may be limited to community service or extracurricular activities. That's okay! Employers just want to see that you've actually done something.

Sample Résumé

Building a solid résumé is a key step toward landing a job. Take a look at the sample below. What do you see that you might want to add to your résumé?

JOHN Q. PUBLIC

402111 Little Drive | Lamponia, TN 13579
johnp@email.com | 555.123.4567

RESULTS

Named "Employee of the Month" three times in the past year at Jeffrey's Grille. Youngest coaching assistant for Lamponia Middle School wrestling team. Saved a life through CPR. More to come.

EDUCATION

Washington High School
Projected graduation date: May 20XX | GPA: 3.4

WORK EXPERIENCE

YMCA, Lamponia (20XX–present)
- Ensured safety of all patrons at the swimming pool
- Coordinated swimming instructions for 50 students each summer

Jeffrey's Grille, Lamponia (20XX–present)
- Managed prepping station for salads and fries
- Provided a clean dining environment by wiping off tables and cleaning dishes

VOLUNTEER POSITIONS

Coaching Assistant, Lamponia Middle School | Wrestling Program (20XX–20XX)
- Exercised quick decision-making skills to coach wrestlers during matches
- Planned and instructed practices, including skills training for 32 wrestlers
- Prepared facilities for tournaments including coordinating concessions, referees and scorekeepers

EXTRACURRICULAR ACTIVITIES

Junior Varsity Wrestling Team, Lamponia High School (20XX–present)
Iron Man Award

Wrestling Clubs
Thompson County Wrestling Club, Hopeville Jr. Wrestling Club, Lamponia Wrestling Club

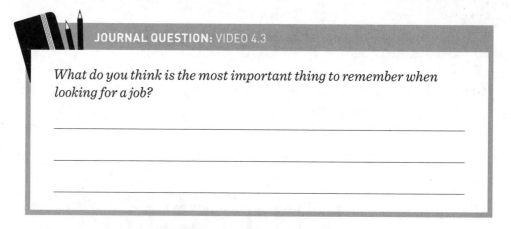

JOURNAL QUESTION: VIDEO 4.3

What do you think is the most important thing to remember when looking for a job?

_____

_____

_____

VIDEO 4.4

Interviews: Dave's Advice

» Present yourself well. You are the _____, so make it the best one available. Be on _____, address everyone by _____, offer a firm, confident _____, and maintain _____ contact at all times.

» Designate a time to _____ _____ after the interview —and DO IT!

 How Can I Land a Job Without Any Experience?

"What kind of things can you put on a part-time job application that will make you stand out from everyone else?"

DAVE'S ANSWER: Experience is a great thing to have when you're looking for a job. Every employer wants to know that a potential employee can do the job.

But even if it's your first "real" job, you probably have experience you didn't think about. Baby-sitting is great experience. It's even better if the parents will give you a good recommendation. If parents feel comfortable with you caring for their child, surely a fast-food manager can trust you to flip a few burgers.

If you're in band, hold a seat on the student council, or even play sports, these things can catch a manager's eye. They all show that you're willing to work, commit to something, and take on responsibility.

Interview Basics

Before an Interview

» Research the company. You will need to be prepared to answer questions such as, "What do you know about our company?" and "Why do you want to work here?"

» Practice with a friend and prepare to answer commonly asked interview questions (you can research these online).

During the Interview

» Dress professionally and be well-groomed.

» Do not slouch or chew gum.

» Arrive 10 to 15 minutes early.

» Be personable. Connect with the interviewer.

» Be yourself. You will be perceived as authentic and trustworthy.

» Be organized. Bring extra copies of your résumé and a notepad to jot things down.

» Keep it positive. Never say anything negative about past employers or work experiences.

» Show interest and be enthusiastic. Ask questions that build on your interview discussion.

"Think beyond your lifetime if you want to accomplish something truly worthwhile."

WALT DISNEY
American animator, film producer, entrepreneur and philanthropist

In American culture, too many people spend a lifetime chasing wealth in a career that they hate. Or they work an excessive number of hours every week. "Do not wear yourself out to get rich; have the wisdom to show restraint" (Proverbs 23:4). Do something you love and that is fun for you! If you make a lot of money, great! But if you don't, at least you will have spent a lifetime doing something that was rewarding. Money should never become your primary motivation.

TAXPAYER OBLIGATIONS, INTEREST AND PENALTIES

As a taxpayer, there are certain legal obligations you are expected to meet when managing your taxes. If you fail to pay your taxes on time, it can result in IRS penalties, and in turn, compounding interest that can make your tax debt much larger. The IRS has the power to garnish your pay, take money from your bank account, or place a lien against or seize your personal property.

Interview Basics *(Continued)*

» Do not bring up the issue of salary during your first interview. Find out all you can about the general salary levels of the company beforehand. If the employer asks you about salary expectations, try to give a general answer.

» Ask your interviewer when you can expect to hear from them.

After the Interview

» Take time to write down some notes about anything that might influence your decision of whether or not to accept the position.

» Write a thank-you note to the employer within 48 hours of the interview, even if you are not interested in the job.

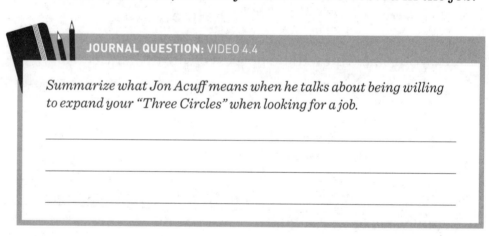

JOURNAL QUESTION: VIDEO 4.4

Summarize what Jon Acuff means when he talks about being willing to expand your "Three Circles" when looking for a job.

_____

_____

_____

Section 5: Income and Taxes

Benjamin Franklin said, "Only two things in life are certain: death and taxes." The government relies on the revenue taxes create to meet their expenses and pay for services such as roads, education and social services. While the specifics differ from state to state, the government taxes three economic bases to pay for its programs: income, consumption and wealth. Like it or not, taxes are a part of everyday life.

Taxes on Income

Income taxes are taxes paid out by anyone who earns an income. April 15 is the day that income tax filings are due in the United States. If you have overpaid throughout the year, you will receive a tax refund. If it is determined that you have underpaid, you will have an additional tax payment due. You will pay both federal and state income taxes (unless you live in a state that does not have an income tax). Income taxes are often subject to deductions or credits based on individual financial circumstances.

On your pay stub, you will notice three taxes taken out or deducted from your paycheck. These are commonly referred to as withholdings. When you are hired by a company, you will fill out a federal tax form called a W-4. The information on this form is the basis for determining how much income tax should be withheld from your paycheck. Payroll taxes, as these are commonly known, are a tax on income. Hence, you file an income tax return with the government every year you earn income.

The Three Taxes Are:

1. **Federal income tax**, which is used to support government programs. This is where the federal government gets much of its money. You work. They spend.

2. **State income tax**, which is used to support state services (if you work in a state without a state income tax, you will not have this withholding)

When you get your first job, you will quickly notice that a portion of your pay is taken out of your check for taxes. Taxes are a required contribution to local, state and federal governments and are used to fund government programs, infrastructure and agencies such as the military, public schools and roads.

THE INTERNAL REVENUE SERVICE (IRS)
The IRS is the federal government agency responsible for tax collection and tax law enforcement. It was created during the Civil War in 1862 to enact a national income tax to pay for war expenses.

3. **FICA (Federal Insurance Contribution Act) tax** funds Social Security and Medicare benefits through ongoing payroll tax withholdings. Your employer will pay half of the tax and you will pay the other half. Your FICA tax withholding will generally appear as two separate taxes on your pay stub: Social Security (SOC SEC or SOC) and Medicare (MEDICARE or MED).

Taxes on Wealth

The primary tax on wealth is property tax.

» Property tax is the main source of revenue for local governments. Taxes on land, private homes and business property are property taxes.

» Some states tax certain types of personal property. This might include cars, boats and recreational vehicles.

» Taxes on wealth include inheritance, estate and gift taxes.

Taxes on Consumption

The primary taxes on consumption are sales and excise tax.

» **Sales tax** is tax on goods and services that goes to your state or local government. Sales tax is used by states as a source of their income, and each state sets its own tax rate.

» **Excise tax** is levied on certain goods produced within a country and is sometimes referred to as luxury tax. This is used by both the state and federal government. Taxes on items such as gasoline, beer, liquor, cigarettes and airplane tickets are excise taxes.

Three Types of Income

⁎ NOTE: All types of income are taxed.

1. **Earned income:** Any income (wages/salary) that is generated by working. Earned income is taxed at a higher rate than any other type of income.

2. **Portfolio income:** Income generated by selling an investment at a higher price than you paid for it. Portfolio income is sometimes referred to as "capital gains" because that's how the money is taxed by the federal government. Portfolio income is often taxed at very high rates, sometimes as high as earned income.

3. **Passive income:** Money earned on a regular basis with little or no effort required to maintain it. Some things that produce passive income are real estate, intellectual property like books or internet content, or a business in which the owner is not actively involved. Passive income often allows for the most favorable tax treatment.

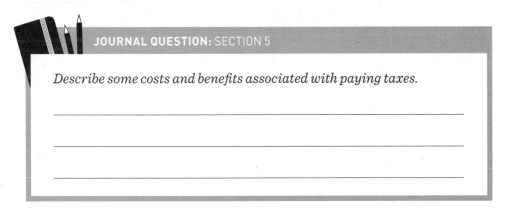

JOURNAL QUESTION: SECTION 5

Describe some costs and benefits associated with paying taxes.

_____

_____

_____

Budget Builder

As your income changes, so will your budget! Go to foundationsU.com/11 for your next budget lesson.

In the latest annual survey for the *National Association of Colleges and Employers*, companies planning to hire were most interested in grads who had majored in engineering, business, accounting, computer science or economics. Unfortunately, many students prefer majors such as social sciences, history, education and psychology, which aren't in high demand.

Chapter Summary

 ## Check for Understanding

Now it's time to check your learning! Go back to the Before You Begin section for this chapter. Place a checkmark next to the learning outcomes you've mastered. Review the Measure Your Progress section.

 ## Big Ideas

The following Big Ideas are intended to provide clear focus and purpose to the lessons. Read each statement and think about how what you've learned will affect your current and future decisions. Then, in the space provided, write an "I believe" statement for each of the Big Ideas.

» Know your personal strengths and weaknesses.

_____

» Set goals.

_____

» Taxes on income include federal, state and FICA taxes.

_____

Take Action Challenge

Create your résumé. If you already have a résumé, compare it to our sample in Section 4 and make sure that it has each component. Remember, your résumé will require updating every time you change jobs or complete different education levels. Go to foundationsU.com/resume to access a quick and easy résumé building tool.

Build On What You've Learned

Use the graphic organizer below to describe the three types of income.

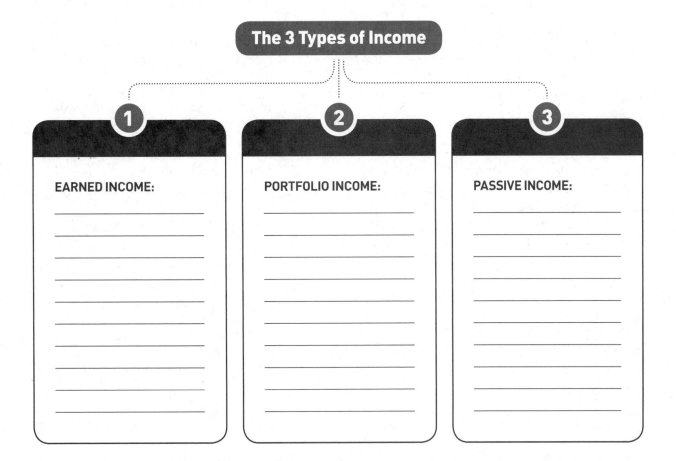

The 3 Types of Income

1

EARNED INCOME:

2

PORTFOLIO INCOME:

3

PASSIVE INCOME:

Money in Review

Matching

Match the following terms to the correct definition below.

A Cover Letter   D Property Taxes   G Social Security

B Portfolio Income E Résumé   H Income Tax

C Personal Branding F Earned Income

1. _____ The process by which we "market" ourselves to others; involves highlighting personal strengths, interests and unique qualities and identifying goals

2. _____ Taxes paid out by anyone who earns an income

3. _____ A letter that is always accompanied by a résumé; used to inform a prospective employer of your interest and capabilities as they relate to a specific employment opportunity

4. _____ A brief account of one's professional or work experience and qualifications

5. _____ Income generated by selling an investment at a higher price than you paid for it

6. _____ A federal insurance program funded by taxpayer dollars that provides benefits to people who are retired, unemployed or disabled

7. _____ Any income (wages/salary) that is generated by working

8. _____ Taxes paid by anyone who owns property such as land, a home or commercial real estate

Illustration

Draw a picture representation of each of the following terms.

Networking

Passive Income

Multiple Choice
Circle the correct answer.

9. Once you've defined your dream, your goals should be the practical application of how you're going to accomplish your dream.

   A True
   B False

10. Taxes are an optional contribution to local, state and federal governments.

    A True
    B False

11. The Internal Revenue Service (IRS) is the federal government agency responsible for

    A Writing tax laws
    B Tax collection and tax law enforcement
    C Keeping the unemployment rate low
    D Filling out your tax forms

12. What is the difference between gross pay and net pay?

    A Gross pay describes your pay after deductions; net pay is before
    B Gross and net pay are the same
    C Net pay describes your pay after deductions; gross pay is before
    D None of the above

13. Sales tax and excise tax are both taxes on

    A Wealth
    B Income
    C Property
    D Consumption

Short Answer
Respond in the space provided.

14. Would you do something you did not like in order to make a higher income? Why or why not?

    _____
    _____
    _____

15. Why is it important to understand different personality styles?

    _____
    _____
    _____

16. What are some important things to do when interviewing for a job?

    _____
    _____
    _____

17. What is the difference between gross and net income?

    _____
    _____
    _____

18. Jon gave you a great deal of practical information on achieving success and reaching your goals. What was your biggest takeaway from his lesson?

    _____
    _____
    _____

CHAPTER 12

What do other high school students know about giving to others?

We asked teens to describe something—big or small—they had done to help others.

....

"I created a charity organization called 'Cash for Candy' to help a little girl in Guatemala pay for a surgery her family could not afford."

Junior, New York

"I listen when anyone needs someone to talk to and give some helpful advice."

Freshman, Kansas

"I did a food drive for a family who lost their house in a fire awhile ago."

Senior, Connecticut

"I have helped others by doing service projects with my Boy Scout Troop."

Senior, South Dakota

Giving

65%

of households give to charity.*

98%

of high-net-worth households give to charity.*

MANY HIGH SCHOOL students want to help others; they are just not sure how to go about it. It's easy as a young adult to see someone in need—a charity that you care about, a ministry that matters—and feel helpless because you don't have a lot of money to give. Finding extra time and resources to help others is not always easy. In this chapter we are going to highlight the importance of serving others and help you identify ways you can give . . . starting now!

*National Philanthropic Trust

Before You Begin

 Learning Outcomes

Once you've completed this chapter's videos, you will be asked to return to this list of learning outcomes and place a checkmark next to the items you've mastered.

Section 1: False Perceptions

☐ Identify your core values.

☐ Identify your own specific talents and evaluate ways you could use those talents to help others.

Section 2: Make an Impact

☐ Identify ways in which giving benefits both the giver and the receiver.

Section 3: Give Your Time and Talents

☐ Identify various types of charitable giving (time, money, talents).

☐ Examine various areas of need in your own community.

☐ Identify a variety of charitable organizations.

Section 4: Define Your Legacy

☐ Explain the concept of leaving a legacy.

☐ Illustrate the importance of giving to others throughout your life, starting now.

 Key Terms

Get to know the language of money.

» **Core Values:** Traits or qualities that represent an individual's highest priorities, deeply held beliefs and motivating forces; one's guiding principles

» **Legacy:** Anything handed down from the past; something that someone has achieved that continues to exist after they are gone

» **Nonprofits:** Organizations that use money raised to achieve their goals rather than distributing them as profit

» **Philanthropy:** Means "love of humanity"; identifying and exercising one's values in giving and volunteering

Measure Your Progress

Before watching the video, read each statement below and mark whether you agree or disagree in the "Before" column. Then, after watching the video, do it again using the "After" column to see if you changed your mind on any statement.

BEFORE			AFTER	
Agree	**Disagree**		**Agree**	**Disagree**
☐	☐	1. I can name three national or international charitable organizations where I have recently volunteered my time or would like to volunteer in the near future.	☐	☐
☐	☐	2. I would like to help others, but I don't know how to go about doing it.	☐	☐
☐	☐	3. I can list five of my core values or principles in which I strongly believe.	☐	☐
☐	☐	4. I can think of three families and/or organizations in my community that need my help.	☐	☐
☐	☐	5. Only people who have a lot of money are able to help those in need.	☐	☐

JOURNAL QUESTION: INTRODUCTION

Do you feel as though giving is an important part of your financial plan? Why or why not?

_____

_____

_____

SECTION 1

DESCRIBE THE MOST RECENT THING YOU HAVE GIVEN TO OTHERS:

"I worked in my church's nursery this week."

Sophomore, Maryland

"I volunteered my time to watch a special needs child, and it was the most rewarding experience. I got more joy out of it just by seeing the little girl's smile."

Junior, Mississippi

"I volunteer at our local nursing home on Tuesdays and Thursdays after school."

Senior, Ohio

"I help our elderly neighbor with her grocery shopping every month since she can't drive."

Junior, Missouri

CHAPTER 12

Section 1: False Perceptions

VIDEO 1.1

I Am Just One

5 ▶ THE FIFTH FOUNDATION
Build Wealth and Give

CONGRATULATIONS! You have made it to the end of your personal finance course. We've taught you to save, budget, avoid debt, invest and . . . give? Well that's really what this chapter is about. If you follow the principles we've taught you, you will achieve wealth. That's so exciting! But managing money isn't just about wealth. Remember when we said that money is like a mirror: It reflects what's important to the person who holds it. We can't complete a course on personal finance without talking about the joy and value of helping others. That's why the Fifth Foundation is Build Wealth and Give.

» We often hear about people who are hurting—families with no food, adults with no homes, kids with no parents.

» In these moments, our world can seem so big. We might think, "I wish I could do something," but at the same time realize, "I am just _____ person."

» The good news is, you *can* make a huge difference in the life of someone else, even if your action is _____.

» One of the most important and rewarding things you can do is _____!

Giving money away produces more joy than anything money can buy. And time spent helping and serving others can be just as meaningful. You might only be one person, but *you* can make a difference!

What the World Says About You

Maybe you're already wanting to help others, but you're just not sure how to go about it. You might even feel okay not helping because it doesn't seem like you can afford it. You'll give when you're older, when you've got a bigger bank account. That's when you'll really be able to make a difference, anyway!

» The fact is, you can get started right away with what you've got _____. That means, if you're working, you can use a portion of your money to benefit someone else.

» But even if you don't have money to give, you've still got YOU! Start with what you have today and give of _____ by volunteering your time and talents.

» To do that, first you'll need to know what _____ to you.

"Some people give time, some money, some their skills and connections, some literally give their life's blood. But everyone has something to give."

BARBARA BUSH
Former First Lady of the United States

Recent studies show that the largest source of charitable giving came from individuals at $217.79 billion, or 73% of total giving; followed by foundations ($41.67 billion/14%), bequests ($24.41 billion/8%) and corporations ($14.55 billion/5%).

National Philanthropic Trust

CHARITABLE ORGANIZATION: An organization set up to provide help and raise money for those in need

AID: To give money, food or other help to a country or organization that needs it

What the World Says About You (Continued)

At times, our culture can send you the message that, as a teen, all you really care about is your cell phone, music and hanging out with friends. You might begin to feel like, *Is that it? Is that who I am?* You mistake society's portrayal of teenagers *as your own reflection.*

» Don't be fooled! The reality is, you are _____.

» Begin the process of discovering the real you! We're talking about your _____, your interests and your passions. The things that make you, YOU.

» Before you can help others, you've got to know your own _____—the things that matter most to you.

Knowing what you value will help you select an organization or charity to serve. If you can identify your talents, you can discover more specific ways to serve. You may not have a steady income in your life right now, but that doesn't mean you have nothing to offer. Giving can be in the form of time, money or abilities.

What Do You Value Most?

*Circle the **10** qualities that are most important to you from the list below.*

respectful	giving	accepting	committed	assertive
trustworthy	unique	sensitive	energetic	cooperative
spiritual	leader	kind	helpful	creative
forgiving	compassionate	joyful	self-controlled	persistent
confident	accountability	humorous	excellence	fair
loving	peaceful	honest	communication	unifying
hard-working	loyal	patient	intellect	competitive

Now List Your Top 3
These are the qualities you value the most, or your core values.

1    2   3

Your Values

Your values make you, YOU. People generally give of themselves to causes that are important to them. Your values are the beliefs and attitudes that guide your daily behavior. When you decide to help others, make sure that you focus on a need that you can be passionate about and that is in line with your personal values.

You've identified what is important to you. Now let's see what you're good at. Everyone has talents and gifts that can be used to help others.

Here are some examples of how other high school students have used their talents to help others:

» Maggie loves working with animals. She and her family have raised four guide dogs for the blind.

» Charlene's friends say that she has a kindness about her and a gift for putting others at ease. She knows what it's like to be a new student in a big school because her family moved when she was in middle school. Now she makes it a point to reach out to other new students to make them feel welcome.

» Tim is excellent in math and offers free tutoring to his peers after school two days a week.

» Frank is a star basketball player at his high school. On Saturday mornings he volunteers to referee youth games at his local community center.

APPLYING YOUR GIFTS

List some of your talents and hobbies.

1. _____

2. _____

3. _____

Now think of one way you could use one of your talents to help others.

_____

_____

_____

_____

"The happiest people in the world are those who do the most for others."

BOOKER T. WASHINGTON
American educator, author and speaker

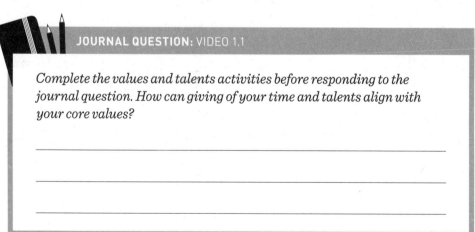

JOURNAL QUESTION: VIDEO 1.1

Complete the values and talents activities before responding to the journal question. How can giving of your time and talents align with your core values?

_____

_____

_____

Section 2: Make an Impact

Americans give billions of dollars to charities every year.

National Philanthropic Trust

OUTREACH: The practice of providing help and advice to people in a community before they have to ask for it

DONOR: Someone who gives things such as money or goods to an organization, especially one that helps people

VIDEO 2.1

Open Hands Build Wealth

Money is important, but people are more important. Being wealthy is not an end—it is a means to an end. That end is helping people. The truth is, when you hold your money with a clenched fist, it destroys your relationships. You end up placing more value on money than people. So make a decision right now to put people first.

» When you hold your money with an _____ hand, life looks a lot different. [10]

» It may take a little longer to reach your financial goals, but you're investing in something far more _____. [11]

» When you give, you _____ a person's life permanently. [12]

» The joy of giving lasts longer than the happy feeling you get when you spend money on _____. [13]

» It's okay to spend money on yourself. Just make sure you spend money to _____ other people as well. [14]

» Need another reason to give? It's just plain _____! [15]

You don't need a lot of money to help others. You just need to be willing to start. We think that giving 10% of your income is a good goal. If that's too much, then just give what you can. If you don't have any money to give, no problem! Give of your time, your talents, your energy. The point is, you *can* give. The measure of a person is not how much money they make, it's how they use the money and how they help others.

Case Study: Finding Comfort in Giving

A teenager in Ohio was grieving over the death of her 89-year-old great-grandmother. "Some of her last words were, 'I don't want anybody to be upset.'" But Samantha was upset. She decided, "Maybe I can't be happy right now, but I can do things to make other people happy."

Samantha began doing small acts of kindness, like paying for the meal of a person behind her in line at McDonald's. She decided that, in honor of her grandmother, she would perform 89 random acts of kindness. She discovered that seeing the reaction of people made her feel good.

Over time, Samantha's giving included buying meals for others at restaurants, donating items to the Humane Society, and baking a birthday cake for a friend. She enjoyed giving so much that she began to inspire others to give on her Facebook page *89 Acts of Kindness*. She offered packets with good-deed suggestions that included a photo and bio of her late grandmother, Virginia.

Doing good for others was a fitting tribute to Virginia. "She was like the Golden Rule put in motion," Samantha said. "And she was a really big influence in my life."

Give Now and Always

John D. Rockefeller was a businessman in the late 1800s and early 1900s. He became one of the wealthiest people in America during his lifetime. But Rockefeller is not just remembered for his wealth. It's what he *did* with his money that we remember him for generations later.

Rockefeller spent the last 40 years of his life as a philanthropist. The money he gave made huge progress in _____, medicine and scientific research. [16] He also gave generously to churches, built hospitals and colleges, and was even well-known for handing out money to people as he walked down the street.

Rockefeller began giving long before he became rich. He understood the importance of starting small and gave out of his first paycheck, which was only $1.50. He _____ [17] giving when he didn't have much money, and he continued to give as his salary grew into the hundreds, thousands and eventually millions.

81% of high-net-worth donors cite "giving back to the community" as a chief motivation for giving.

National Philanthropic Trust

"Wealth is a sacred trust to be managed for the good of others."

ANDREW CARNEGIE
American industrialist and philanthropist

TIPS FOR DONATING MONEY

1. Be proactive in your giving. Take time to identify which causes are most important to you.

2. Check the charity's commitment to accountability and transparency.

3. Obtain copies of the charity's financial records and determine what percentage of funds raised are used on salaries and overhead (cost of running the organization). You should feel confident that most of the money you give is concentrated on the cause you are supporting and not on administration costs.

4. Concentrate your giving on just a few well-run organizations. Unlike investing, when spending your charitable dollars, diversification is not a good thing.

5. Make a long-term commitment. Smart donors support their favorite charities for the long haul.

Make Giving a Priority
Giving is the first category in the Student Budget form as a reminder to always put giving first!

GIVING	Ⓑ▸ Budgeted
Charity	$_____
Other:_____	$_____
Ⓒ▸ GIVING TOTAL:	$_____

SAVING	Budgeted
Emergency Fund	$_____
College	$_____
Car & Repairs	$_____

🚗 TRANSPORTATION	Budgeted
Gas	$_____
Car Insurance	$_____
Oil Changes	$_____
License & Taxes	$_____
TRANSPORTATION TOTAL:	$_____

👤 PERSONAL	Budgeted
Cosmetics / Hair Care	$_____
Music / Technology	$_____

Give Now and Always *(Continued)*

By starting where you are today, you _____ character for the future. [18]

The more you give, the more you are fulfilled and the more you want to give. It's a great cycle to be on. Giving is not a matter of moving money from your wallet to a charity or collection plate; it is a matter of realizing that there are others less fortunate than you and you have a genuine desire to help them. Money is just one way to do that.

By helping someone, you give them encouragement, hope and relief. The more people you help, the more joy you will experience!

JOURNAL QUESTION: VIDEO 2.1

When you are doing your monthly budget, why do you think it is important to have "giving" placed at the very top?

_____

_____

_____

Section 3:
Give Your Time and Talents

VIDEO 3.1

Money Is Not the Only Way to Give

Giving is one of the most important and rewarding parts of your financial journey. Since you are going to make sure that you stay completely debt free, you will have that much more money to spend, invest and give. Just remember that money given produces more joy than it could ever buy!

As you are working toward your financial goals, like saving your $500 emergency fund, money to give may seem hard to come by. That's when you can find creative ways to give. You can give your time, your talents, your knowledge or your services to help other people.

» Our culture is so "me" focused.

» A powerful thing happens when we _____ others— we stop focusing on ourselves. We stop being consumed by our own struggles, our looks and the things *we* want. [19]

» When we give to others we are saying, "Right now the needs of this person matter _____." That's why giving more than money—giving of yourself—is so powerful! [20]

» Andy Stanley says, "Giving up something now for something better later is not a sacrifice. It is an _____." [21]

Each person you give to produces a new story and a new thrill. It is a feeling that never grows dull. Having fun with money is good, but you will tire of movies and clothes. In a way, giving is a lot like compound interest— you put some in, but you get much

more out! Try it! When you're in line at a coffee shop, offer to pay for the coffee of the person behind you and see how it makes you feel. That feeling and the feeling of the person your generosity impacted is much more valuable than $5!

"You've got to live like no one else so later you can GIVE like no one else!"

DAVE RAMSEY

TIPS FOR DONATING NON-CASH ITEMS

1. Determine whether or not the items you wish to donate are useful.

2. Consider selling your items and donating the proceeds to charity. Donating cash instead of goods allows charities greater flexibility in spending the money so that it reaches people who need it the most.

3. Start locally to find the right charity in order to avoid transportation costs that can lower the impact of your donation.

"Volunteers are not paid not because they are worthless, but because they are priceless."

AUTHOR UNKNOWN

GIVING IS CONTAGIOUS
Amidst holiday cheer, a customer in the drive-thru line of a local coffee shop decided to pay for the coffee of the customer behind him. He had no idea that his small act of kindness would spark three full hours of giving. A total of 228 customers who followed decided to "pay it forward" by paying for the coffee of the person behind them in line! People inside the store joined in the fun as well. "There was a lot of energy in the store," said the general manager. "Our team was really excited and shouting out the number of pay-it-forwards all morning."

"The best thing about giving of ourselves is that what we get is always better than what we give. The reaction is greater than the action."

ORISON SWETT MARDEN
American author

Ways You Can Give Now

Here are some practical ways you can volunteer in your community. This is just a start. Be creative! Consider your personal talents and skills.

» With every season, clean out the clothes you no longer use and donate them to your local homeless shelter. Get your friends involved so that, together, you can donate even more!

» Offer to tutor a peer or younger child who is struggling in a subject you happen to be good at. Your school counselor may be able to help set this up.

» Offer to be a mentor to an underprivileged youth in your community.

» Volunteer to help at a Special Olympics event.

» Volunteer at your local animal shelter.

» Adopt a senior citizen as a friend/mentor and commit to spending time with him/her each week.

» Rake leaves, shovel snow, or clean gutters for a senior citizen.

» Teach Sunday school.

» Participate in a 5k run for your favorite charity.

» Befriend new students and eat lunch with them, introduce them to your friends, and offer to help them find a class, etc.

» Write a letter or send a care package to a soldier overseas.

» Write a thank you letter to a teacher who had a positive effect on you.

» Do extra chores around your house without being asked.

» Help a younger brother or sister with his or her homework.

JOURNAL QUESTION: VIDEO 3.1

List some areas of need in your school or community (youth programs, homeless shelter, humane society, recycling, roadside cleanup, nursing home, etc.).

1. _____

2. _____

3. _____

Section 4: Define Your Legacy

Legacy

Why are we talking so much about giving? Wasn't this course supposed to be about personal _____? How is giving connected?
₂₂

The act of giving—putting yourself out there for the sake of another person, building relationships, and sacrificing your time and energy—creates a legacy. It gives _____
to the journey of your life.
₂₃

You can be remembered for any number of things:

» athletic ability	» anger
» musical gifts	» attitude
» sense of humor	» selfishness
» kindness	» generosity

What you can do today—yes, even in high school—is ask yourself, *How do I want to be remembered?*

You can make a lot of money and be wildly successful; you can go after your dreams and accomplish each and every one of them. But to what end? If you're giving of yourself, you're building a legacy to be proud of. After all, your _____ is the *impact you have on the world*—and it shows the world what really matters to you.
₂₄

The top four national volunteer activities are fundraising (26.6%), food collection or distribution (23.5%), general labor or transportation (20.5%), and tutoring or teaching (19%).

National Philanthropic Trust

"Let us not be satisfied with just giving money. Money is not enough, money can be got, but they need your hearts to love them. So, spread your love everywhere you go."

MOTHER TERESA
Indian Roman Catholic nun

There are approximately 1 million charitable organizations in the United States.

National Philanthropic Trust

TAX BENEFITS OF GIVING
Your primary motivation for giving should be the simple desire to help others. However, since this is a course on personal finance, we also want you to be aware of the great tax benefits that come with giving. Here are some things you should know.

- A gift to a qualified charitable organization may entitle you to a charitable contribution deduction against your income tax if you itemize deductions.

- A contribution to a qualified charity is deductible in the year in which it is paid.

- Most, but not all, charitable organizations qualify for a charitable contribution deduction.

- There are limits to how much you can deduct, but they're very high.

- Certain rules exist for non-cash donations.

- Remember to document your charitable contributions.

TAX DEDUCTION: A reduction in the gross amount of income on which a tax is calculated

Summary of the Five Foundations

1 THE FIRST FOUNDATION
Save a $_____ Emergency Fund
25

2 THE SECOND FOUNDATION
Get Out of _____
26

3 THE THIRD FOUNDATION
Pay _____ for Your Car
27

4 THE FOURTH FOUNDATION
Pay Cash for _____
28

5 THE FIFTH FOUNDATION
Build _____ and _____
29   30

We know that by following these steps, you will build wealth. The sky is the _____! As you do, be intentional with your money. Take care of your needs and commit to helping others along the way! Keeping an open hand and an open _____ means you will leave behind an amazing legacy someday.
31
32

The bottom line is, as a high school student, you've got the opportunity to take all of the _____ _____ we've taught you and apply them to your own situation. You control your future! That's so exciting! You've got your whole life ahead of you. Where you're from, your family background, what you've been told by others—those things don't define you. YOU define you. Success isn't easy, but it's _____ for anyone who is willing to go after it.
33
34

So what *will* your future look like? What *will* your legacy be?

A Message From Jon
The Generosity of Future Me

It would be silly to pretend there are two different people working the same day under the same name, Jon Acuff, but you'd be surprised how many people do that when it comes to money. Especially regarding the "G" word.

I'm talking about giving. When you get intense about beating debt (and reaching other money goals), sometimes it's easy to make the mistake of thinking that giving is something that will come later. And when we talk about later, it's fun to imagine how generous future me is going to be.

"Right now, giving doesn't really fit into the plan. But in the future? Down the road? I'm going to be like Bill Gates! I'll probably just rent a hot air balloon and drop stacks of cash out of it. I'll play Natasha Bedingfield music as I do this and get people dancing and really enjoying the full depth of my amazing generosity. Gonna change the world, man, really change the world."

But you know the truth about "future me"? He or she is incredibly slippery. Just when you think the future has finally arrived, something else comes up. Something more important or critical or ... well, I can start giving later.

You want to beat debt and have long-term success with everything Dave Ramsey talks about? Say good night to future me. Start giving today. Budget some giving right now. You don't have to go crazy. Giving time and money is important no matter where you are in the Five Foundations, that's why Dave put it at the top of the student budget form!

The truth is, future me won't know how to be generous with a lot unless present me learns how to be generous with a little.

So give a little.

Budget Builder

Okay everyone, we've shown you how and why to give to those in need. Now it's time to commit. Go to foundationsU.com/12 to make giving first in your budget.

> "We make a living by what we get, we make a life by what we give."

WINSTON CHURCHILL
Former Prime Minister of the United Kingdom

Recent studies show that the majority of charitable dollars go to churches (32%), education (13%), human services (12%), and grant-making foundations (9%).

National Philanthropic Trust

JOURNAL QUESTION: VIDEO 4.1

When have you been impacted because someone gave their time, money or talents to help you? How did this affect you?

_____

_____

_____

Chapter Summary

Check for Understanding

Now it's time to check your learning! Go back to the Before You Begin section for this chapter. Place a checkmark next to the learning outcomes you've mastered and complete the "after" column of the Measure Your Progress section.

Build On What You've Learned

Fill in the graphic organizer with each of the Five Foundations. Put a checkmark next to each of the foundations you have accomplished.

COMPLETE?		THE FIVE FOUNDATIONS (WRITE THESE OUT)
☐	**1**	THE FIRST FOUNDATION _____
☐	**2**	THE SECOND FOUNDATION _____
☐	**3**	THE THIRD FOUNDATION _____
☐	**4**	THE FOURTH FOUNDATION _____
☐	**5**	THE FIFTH FOUNDATION _____

Big Ideas

The following Big Ideas are intended to provide clear focus and purpose to the lessons. Read each statement and think about how what you've learned will affect your current and future decisions. Then, in the space provided, write an "I believe" statement for each of the Big Ideas.

» People are more important than money.

_____

» Discover your values, interests and passions—then give!

_____

» Your legacy is the impact you make on the world.

_____

Take Action Challenge

Look at your Five Foundations chart. For each foundation that you have not completed, write a brief summary of how you intend to meet that goal. Be sure to include a time goal for each of the foundations.

STEPS TO MEET YOUR FOUNDATION GOAL	TIME
1 _____	_____
2 _____	_____
3 _____	_____
4 _____	_____
5 _____	_____

Money in Review

Matching
Match the following terms to the correct definition below.

A Legacy   **C** Nonprofits   **E** The Fourth Foundation

B Core Values   **D** The First Foundation   **F** Philanthropy

1. _____ Organizations that use money raised to achieve their goals rather than distributing them as profit

2. _____ Means "love of humanity"; identifying and exercising one's values in giving and volunteering

3. _____ Pay cash for college

4. _____ Anything handed down from the past; something that someone has achieved that continues to exist after they are gone

5. _____ Save a $500 emergency fund

6. _____ Traits or qualities that represent an individual's highest priorities, deeply held beliefs and motivating forces; one's guiding principles

Illustration
Draw a picture representation of each of the following terms.

Charitable Giving

Your Core Values

Multiple Choice

Circle the correct answer.

7. You have to wait until you have a large income before you can help others.

    Ⓐ True
    Ⓑ False

8. One financial benefit of giving money to charity is that your contribution may be tax deductible.

    Ⓐ True
    Ⓑ False

9. Which of the following should be a consideration when selecting a nonprofit to which you'd like to contribute?

    Ⓐ Your values and beliefs
    Ⓑ The charity's commitment to accountability and transparency
    Ⓒ How well run the organization is
    Ⓓ All of the above

10. Is it better to give to many charities or just a few?

    Ⓐ Many
    Ⓑ Just a few
    Ⓒ Doesn't matter
    Ⓓ None at all

11. What percentage of households give to charity?

    Ⓐ 100%
    Ⓑ 20%
    Ⓒ 65%
    Ⓓ 5%

Short Answer

Respond in the space provided.

12. Why is it important to give money, time or talents?

    _____
    _____
    _____

13. What does it mean to leave a legacy?

    _____
    _____
    _____

14. Write down something you learned in this chapter.

    _____
    _____
    _____

15. If you could start a charity, what would it be? Who would you help and in what way? Why?

    _____
    _____
    _____

16. How can giving to others have a positive impact on you?

    _____
    _____

Glossary

401(k): Defined contribution plan offered by a corporation to its employees, which allows employees to set aside tax-deferred income for retirement purposes; in some cases, employers will match their contributions

403(b): Retirement plan similar to a 401(k) plan, but one that is offered by non-profit organizations, such as hospitals, schools and some charitable organizations, rather than corporations; employees set aside tax-deferred dollars

457 plan: Non-qualified, deferred compensation plan established by state and local governments for tax-exempt government agencies and tax-exempt employers; eligible employees are allowed to make salary deferral contributions to the 457 plan; earnings grow on a tax-deferred basis and contributions are not taxed until the assets are distributed from the plan.

529 plan: College savings plan that allows individuals to save on a tax-deferred basis in order to fund future college and graduate school expenses of a child or beneficiary; generally sponsored by a state, these are professionally managed investments

12b-1 fee: An annual fee that some mutual funds charge to pay for marketing and distribution activities

A

Accelerated payment: Making bi-weekly payments on your mortgage that makes one additional payment on your mortgage annually

Accountability: The quality or state of being responsible, liable or answerable

Adjustable rate mortgage (ARM): Home loan secured by a deed of trust or mortgage in which the interest rate will change periodically (i.e., annually); typically adjusted based on a published index such as the Treasury Bill or LIBOR; brought on as a result of high interest rates in the early 1980s as a way for banks to transfer the risk of higher interest rates to the consumer

Aggressive growth stock mutual fund: Mutual fund that seeks to provide maximum long-term capital growth from stocks of primarily smaller companies or narrow market segments; dividend income is incidental; the most volatile fund; also referred to as a small-cap fund

Allowance: Money given to a child by his/her parent/guardian, typically on a weekly basis

Amoral: Lacking morals; neither good nor bad

Amortization table: Breakdown showing how much of each regular payment will be applied toward principal and how much toward interest over the life of a loan; also shows the gradual decrease of the loan balance until it reaches zero

Annuity: Contract sold by an insurance company, designed to provide payments to the holder at specified intervals, usually after retirement; the holder is taxed at the time of distribution or withdrawal, making this a tax-deferred arrangement

Annual fee: A yearly fee that's charged by the credit card company for the convenience of the credit card

Annual percentage rate (APR): Cost of borrowing money on an annual basis; takes into account the interest rate and other related fees on a loan.

Appreciation: An increase in value

Asset: Anything that is owned by an individual; with respect to saving and investing, assets are generally categorized as liquid (cash) and capital (investment) assets

Asset allocation: The process of deciding how investment dollars will be apportioned among various classes of financial assets, such as stocks, bonds and cash investments

Asset classes: Major categories of financial assets or securities. The three primary classes are common stocks, bonds and cash investments

ATM card: Automated teller card which allows you to make transactions in automated teller machines

Auction: A public sale in which property or items of merchandise are sold to the highest bidder

Auto insurance: Insurance to protect a car owner in the event of an accident or damage to a vehicle

Average annual return: The rate of return on investments averaged over a specific period of time. It is determined by adding together the rates of return for each year and dividing by the number of years in the calculation

B

Back-end load: Sales commission paid when the investor sells mutual fund shares; sometimes phased out over several years; also called redemption fee or contingent-deferred sales charge

Balanced fund: A mutual fund that invests in more than one type of financial asset: stocks, bonds, and in some cases, cash investments

Balloon mortgage: A home loan in which the sum of the monthly payments is insufficient to repay the entire loan; a final payment comes due, which is a lump sum of the remaining principal balance

Bankruptcy: Legal procedure for dealing with debt problems of individuals and businesses; specifically a legal court case filed under one of the chapters of Title 11 of the United States Code (also see Chapter 7 bankruptcy, Chapter 11 bankruptcy, and Chapter 13 bankruptcy)

Bargain: A deal obtained when negotiating and paying a lesser price than asked for an item

Beneficiary: The recipient of assets passed on from the death of a friend or relative

Bond: A debt instrument where an issuer such as a corporation, municipality or government agency owes you money; a form of I.O.U.; the issuer makes regular interest payments on the bond and promises to pay back or redeem the face value of the bond at a specified point in the future (the maturity date)

Bond mutual fund: Mutual funds that buy bonds

Branding: The promotion of a product or service by identifying it with distinct characteristics (usually associated with public perception, quality or effectiveness)

Brand recognition/awareness: Refers to the public's ability to recall and recognize a brand by its logo, jingles, packaging, etc.

Break-even analysis: Method used to evaluate the wisdom of a financial decision by determining the length of time it will take for the cost of the decision to be recouped

Budget: A written cash flow plan

Buyer's remorse: Feeling regret or concern after making a large purchase

C

Capital gain: A positive difference between an asset's price when bought and its price when sold; the opposite of capital loss

Capital gains distribution: Payment to mutual fund shareholders of any gains realized during the year on securities that have been sold at a profit. Capital gains are distributed on a "net" basis after subtracting any capital losses for the year. When losses exceed gains for the year, the difference may be carried forward and subtracted from future gains.

Capital loss: A negative difference between an asset's price when bought and its price when sold; the opposite of capital gain

Carbon check: A copy of each check you write

Career: Your line of work

Cash flow statement: A summary that shows total income and spending for a given time period

Cash investments: Investments in interest-bearing bank deposits, money market instruments and U.S. Treasury Bills or notes

Cash value insurance: Also known as permanent life insurance; premiums include a death benefit and a plan to build savings within the policy; two main types are whole life and universal life; significantly more expensive than term life insurance

Caveat emptor: Latin term for "buyer beware"

C.D.: Certificate of Deposit, usually at a bank; savings account with a slightly higher interest rate because of a longer savings commitment (i.e., six months, one year, etc.)

Chapter 7 Bankruptcy: Chapter of the Bankruptcy Code providing for liquidation of the debtor's assets in order to repay the creditors; certain assets or aggregate value of assets of the debtor may be exempt based on state law

Chapter 11 Bankruptcy: Reorganization bankruptcy, usually involving a corporation or partnership; generally includes a plan of reorganization to keep a business alive and pay creditors over time

Chapter 13 Bankruptcy: Chapter of the Bankruptcy Code providing for an individual to repay debts over time, usually three to five years; debtor makes periodic payments to the bankruptcy trustee, who in turn pays the creditors; sometimes includes adjustments to debt balances within the bankruptcy

Checking account: Account set up to maintain daily financial activities. Users can draft checks for payment, issue deposits into their accounts, and keep track of their debit card transactions through their checking account.

Claim: Paperwork filed with an insurance company in order to get them to cover a loss for someone they insure

Co-insurance: In a health insurance policy, after you pay the deductible the insurance company pays a percentage and you pay a percentage; 80/20–insurance pays 80% and you pay 20%

Collision: Portion of auto insurance that covers losses due to vehicle damage in an accident

Commission: A fee paid for providing a service

Commodities: A food, metal or fixed physical substance that investors buy or sell, usually via future contracts

Communication: A process by which information is exchanged between individuals

Compensation: The total wage or salary and benefits that an employee receives

Compound interest: Interest paid on interest previously earned; credited daily, monthly, quarterly or semi-annually

Comprehensive: Pays for damage to your car that is not a result of an accident

Consignment shop: Retail store where people sell items and the owner of the shop gets a percentage of the sale

Consumer: A person or organization that uses a product or a service

Contact letter: A letter informing a prospective employer that you are interested in working for their company

Contents insurance: Insurance policy that covers personal possessions in a home or apartment

Conventional loan: Mortgage obtained through the Federal National Mortgage Association (FNMA), which insures against default; generally includes a down payment of 5-20% or more

Copay: In regards to health insurance, paying a set amount per medical visit

Core values: Traits or qualities that represent an individual's highest priorities, deeply held beliefs, and motivating forces; one's guiding principles

Cost-benefit analysis: The process of quantifying costs and benefits of a decision

Cover letter: Similar to a contact letter but is used to inform the prospective employer of your interest and capabilities as they relate to a specific employment opportunity; always accompanied by a résumé

Coverage: Applies to the amount of protection you have through an insurance company in the event of a loss

Cosigning: Offering to guarantee someone else's loan; becoming responsible for loan repayment if the borrower defaults

Credit: The granting of a loan and the creation of debt; any form of deferred payment

Credit bureau: An agency which collects the credit history of consumers so that creditors can make decisions about granting loans

Credit card: Tool used to finance a purchase

Credit disability: Insurance that pays for financed items or purchases if you become disabled and are unable to earn an income

Credit Laws:

» **Fair Credit Reporting Act (1971):** Federal law governing the reporting of debt repayment information; establishes when a credit reporting agency may provide a report to someone; states that obsolete information must be taken off (7 to 10 years); gives consumers the right to know what is in their credit report; requires that both a credit bureau and information provider (i.e., department store) have an obligation to correct wrong information; gives consumers the right to dispute inaccurate information and add a 100-word statement to their report to explain accurate negative information; gives consumers the right to know what credit bureau provided the report when they are turned down for credit

» **Fair Credit Billing Act (1975):** Federal law that covers credit card billing problems and applies to all open-end credit accounts (i.e. credit cards and overdraft checking); states that consumers should send a written billing error notice to the creditor within 60 days (after receipt of first bill containing an error), which the creditor must acknowledge in 30 days; requires the creditor to investigate and prohibits them from damaging a consumer's credit rating while a dispute is pending

» **Fair Debt Collection Practices Act (1978):** Federal law that prohibits debt collectors from engaging in unfair, deceptive, or abusive practices when collecting debts; requires collectors to send a written notice stating the name of the creditor and the amount owed; prohibits contacting the consumer if he or she disputes the debt in writing within 30 days (unless collector furnishes proof of the debt); requires collectors to identify themselves on the phone and limits calls to between 8:00 a.m. and 9:00 p.m. unless the consumer agrees to another time; prohibits calling the consumer at work if requested

» **Equal Credit Opportunity Act (1975):** Federal law that ensures consumers are given an equal chance to receive credit; prohibits discrimination on the basis of gender, race, marital status, religion, national origin, age or receipt of public assistance; prohibits lenders from asking about plans to have children, or refusing to consider consistently received alimony or child support payments as income; grants the consumer legal rights to know why he or she was denied credit

» **Truth in Lending Act (1969):** Federal law that mandates disclosure of information about the cost of credit; mandates that the finance charge (i.e., all charges to borrow money, including interest) and the annual percentage rate (APR) must be displayed prominently on forms and statements used by creditors; provides criminal penalties for willful violators, as well as civil remedies; protects against unauthorized use of one's credit card, limiting personal loss to $50 if the card is lost or stolen

» **Fair Credit and Charge Card Disclosure Act (1989):** Portion of the Truth in Lending Act that mandates a section on credit card applications that describes key features and cost (i.e., APR, grace period for purchases, minimum finance charge, balance calculation method, annual fees, transaction fees for cash advances, and penalty fees such as over-the-limit fees and late payment fees)

Credit life: Insurance that pays for financed items or purchases in the event of your death

Credit report: Report showing your payment history

Credit score: A measure of an individual's credit risk; calculated from a credit report using a standardized formula

Credit union: Not-for-profit cooperatives of members with some type of common bond (i.e., employer) that provide a wide array of financial services, often at a lower cost than banks

Currency: Money

D

Day trading: Establishing and liquidating the same position or positions within one day's trading

Debit card: Type of card, often bearing the seal of a major credit card company, issued by a bank and used to make purchases; unlike a credit card, the money comes directly out of a checking account; also called a check card

Debt: An obligation of repayment owed by one party (the debtor/borrower) to a second party (the creditor/lender); in most cases this includes repayment of the original loan amount plus interest

Debt consolidation: Act of combining all debts into one monthly payment, typically extending the terms and the length of time required to repay the debt

Debt snowball: Preferred method of debt repayment; includes a list of all debts organized from smallest to largest balance; minimum payments are made to all debts except for the smallest, which is attacked with the largest possible payments.

Deductible: Amount you must pay before you begin receiving any benefits from your insurance company

Deduction: An amount subtracted from something especially as an allowance against tax

Deed: The legal document conveying title to a property

Deflation: A broad, overall drop in the price of goods and services; the opposite of inflation

Delinquency: Broadly refers to not being current on your payments

Depreciation: A decline in the value of property; the opposite of appreciation

Direct deposit service: A service that electronically transfers all or part of any recurring payment, including dividends, paychecks, pensions and Social Security payments directly to a shareholder's account

Direct transfer: Movement of tax-deferred retirement plan money from one qualified plan or custodian to another; results in no immediate tax liabilities or penalties, but requires IRS reporting

Disability insurance: Policy that insures a worker in the event of an occupational mishap resulting in disability; compensates the injured worker for lost pay

Disposable income: Amount of money left over after all necessities and expenses are paid

Dividend distribution: Payment of income to mutual fund shareholders from interest or dividends generated by the fund's investments

Diversification: The practice of dividing the money a person invests between several different types of investments in order to lower risk

Dividend: Distribution of a portion of a company's earnings, decided by the board of directors, to a class of its shareholders; generally distributed in the form of cash or stock

Down payment: The part of the purchase price of a property that the buyer pays in cash and does not finance with a mortgage

Duplicate checks: Type of checks that make duplicate copies as you write them out

E

Earned income: Any income (wages/salary) that is generated by working

Economy: A system by which goods and services are produced and distributed

Educational Savings Account (ESA): After-tax college fund that grows tax-free for educational uses; eligibility based on parents' annual income

Elimination period: Amount of time that lapses after a disabling event before the insurance company begins to pay benefits

Emergency fund: Five hundred dollars in readily available cash to be used only in the event of an emergency; the goal of the First Foundation

Employee benefit: Something of value that an employee receives in addition to a wage or salary. Examples include health insurance, disability insurance, discounted childcare, etc.

Employer-Sponsored Retirement Savings Program:
Tax-deferred savings plans offered by employers that provide a federal tax deduction, tax-deferral of contributions and earnings, and in some cases employer matching. They include 401(k) plans for corporate employees, 403(b) plans for employees of schools and non-profit organizations, and Section 457 plans for state and local government employees.

Entrepreneur: A person who starts a business

Envelope system: Series of envelopes that are divided into categories (food, entertainment, gas, etc.) and are used to store cash for planned monthly expenses

Equity: The value of a piece of property over and above any mortgage or liabilities related to it

Estate sale: Type of yard sale with more items, usually the entire contents of a household

Excise tax: A tax levied on the purchase of certain non-essential consumer goods such as tobacco, airline tickets, etc.

Expense: The cost of goods or services

Expense ratio: The percentage of a fund's average net assets used to pay annual fund expenses. The expense ratio takes into account management fees, administrative fees, and any 12b-1 marketing fees

Extended replacement cost: Part of homeowner's insurance policy that pays a percentage beyond the insured price of the home for purposes of rebuilding it in the event of a catastrophic loss. If you do not update this, it will not cover the appreciation of your home (e.g. house is insured for $200,000, but the value goes up to $300,000, you are covered for the $200,000 plus whatever the coverage states).

Federal Deposit Insurance Corporation (FDIC): A federal institution that insures bank deposits

Federal Housing Administration (FHA): Federally sponsored agency chartered in 1934 whose stock is currently owned by savings institutions across the United States. The agency buys residential mortgages that meet certain requirements, sells these mortgages in packages, and insures the lenders against loss.

Federal Insurance Contributions Act (FICA):
Government legislations that funds Social Security and Medicare

Federal Reserve System: The monetary authority of the United States, established in 1913, and governed by the Federal Reserve Board located in Washington D.C. The system includes 12 Federal Reserve Banks and is authorized to regulate monetary policy as well as to supervise Federal Reserve member banks, bank holding companies, international operations of US banks, and US operations of foreign banks.

Fee table: A table, placed near the front of a mutual fund's prospectus, disclosing and illustrating the expenses and fees a shareholder will incur

Financial goals: Short-, immediate, and long-term goals that require money and guide a person's future plans and savings decisions

Financial literacy: The knowledge and skill base necessary to be informed consumers and manage their finances effectively

Financial plan: A plan of action that allows a person to meet not only the immediate needs but also their long-term goals

Financial resources: Financial assets that can be accessed when necessary

Financing: To buy an item with credit; paying over time

Fiscal: Having to do with money

Fiscal year: Accounting period covering 12 consecutive months over which a company determines earnings and profits. The fiscal year serves as a period of reference for the company and does not necessarily correspond to the calendar year.

Five Foundations: The five steps to financial success

Fixed annuity: Type of annuity that guarantees a certain rate of return; see annuity

Fixed income securities: Investments, such as bonds, which provide current income from a fixed schedule of interest payments. While the level of income offered by these securities is predetermined and usually stable, their market value may fluctuate

Fixed rate: An interest rate that does not change over time

Forbearance: Agreement of a lender to suspend foreclosure proceedings and allow a debtor to "catch up" a past due account over a specified period of time; lender grants a postponement of loan payments for a set period of time, giving the borrower time to make up for overdue payments

Foreclosure: Process by which the holder of a mortgage sells the property of a homeowner who has not made interest and/or principal payments on time as stipulated in the mortgage contract

Fraud: A seller's intentional deception of a buyer, which is illegal

Free Application for Federal Student Aid (FAFSA): A form that is completed annually by current and prospective college students to determine their eligibility for financial aid

Free spirit: A person who thinks that everything will work out fine and typically hates to deal with the details

Front-end load: Sales commission that is paid up-front when shares of a mutual fund are purchased

Fund family: A group of mutual funds sponsored by the same organization, often offering exchange privileges between funds and combined account statements for multiple funds

Futures: A term used to designate all contracts covering the sale of financial instruments or physical commodities for future delivery on a commodity exchange

G

Garnishment: Court-ordered attachment that allows a lender to take monies owed directly from a borrower's paycheck; only allowed as part of a court judgment

Goal: The result of achievement toward which effort is directed

Grace period: Time period during which a borrower can pay the full balance of credit due with no finance charges

Grant: A form of federal or state financial aid that does not need to be repaid; usually given to students who demonstrate financial need

Gratuity: An amount paid beyond what is required usually to express satisfaction with service quality; also known as a tip

Gross income: A person's total income prior to withholdings and deductions

Gross National Product (GNP): Measures an economy's total income. It is equal to Gross Domestic Product, plus the income abroad accruing to domestic residents, minus income generated in domestic market accruing to non-residents.

Growth and income mutual fund: A fund that buys stocks in larger, more established companies, medium-sized companies or growth stocks; also called a large-cap fund

Growth stock mutual fund: A fund that buys stock in medium-sized companies that have experienced some growth and are still expanding; also called a mid-cap fund

Guaranteed renewable: If you have a 20-year policy, the insurance has to provide coverage after 20 years regardless of health; it will only be more expensive because you are older

Guaranteed replacement cost: Part of homeowner's insurance policy that pays for the full cost of replacing damaged property without a deduction for depreciation and without a dollar limit

H

Health insurance: Covers you in the event of illness or injury

Health savings account (HSA): A health insurance plan for self-employed people containing a large deductible. Money saved in this account grows tax deferred. It can be used for medical care with no penalties and no taxes, and may be kept if unused.

Home equity loan (HEL): Credit line offered by mortgage lenders that allows a homeowner to borrow money against the equity in their home

Home warranty: An agreement that ensures the structural soundness of a home

Homeowner's insurance: Policy that covers a loss due to damage, theft or injury within one's home

House poor: A condition of having a disproportionately high house payment that limits one's ability to maintain the home and/or meet necessities

I

Impulse purchase: An item that is bought without previous planning or consideration of the long-term effects

Income: Earnings from work or investment

Income fund: A mutual fund that invests in bonds and stocks with higher than average dividends

Income risk: The possibility that income from a mutual fund or other investment will decline either as a fund's assets are reinvested or when a fixed income investment matures and is replaced with a lower-yielding investment

Income tax: Tax paid out by anyone who earns an income

Index: A statistical benchmark designed to reflect changes in financial markets or the economy. In investing, indexes are used to measure changes in segments of the stock and bond markets and as standards against which fund managers and investors can measure the performance of their investment portfolios.

Index fund: A mutual fund that seeks to match the performance of a predetermined market benchmark or index

Individual retirement arrangement (IRA): Tax-deferred arrangement for individuals with earned income and their non-income-producing spouses; growth is not taxed until money is withdrawn; contributions to an IRA are often tax-deductible

Inflation: Rate at which the general level of prices for goods and services rise

Inflation hedge: An asset rising in value, which helps one to keep up with the rising cost of inflation. Real estate can be a great inflation hedge.

Integrity: Having to do with a person's honesty and moral attributes

Interest: Charge for borrowed money generally defined as a percentage; money paid to savers and investors by financial institutions, governments, or corporations for the use of their money (such as a 2% return on money held in a savings account)

Interest-only loan: A mortgage where you only pay the interest

Interest rate: Percentage paid to a lender for the use of borrowed money (in debt); percentage earned on invested principal (in investing)

Interest rate risk: The risk that a security or mutual fund will decline in price because of changes in market interest rates

Internal Revenue Service (IRS): Federal agency responsible for the collection of federal taxes, including personal and corporate, Social Security, and excise and gift taxes

International stock mutual fund: Mutual fund that contains international or overseas companies

Introductory rate: An interest rate charged to a customer during the early stages of a loan; the rate often goes up after a specified period of time

Investing: The process of setting money aside to increase wealth over time for long-term financial goals such as retirement

Investment: Account or arrangement in which a person puts his/her money for long-term growth; invested money should not be used for a suggested minimum of five years

Investment advisor/manager: The individual who manages a portfolio of investments; also called a portfolio manager or a money manager

Investment objective: A mutual fund's performance goal, such as long-term capital appreciation, high current income, or tax exempt income

Investors: People investing in securities, such as stocks and bonds, or other investments, to achieve long-term financial goals

Interview: A meeting between an employer and an applicant; the employer asks the applicant questions to assess whether he or she has the right social skills and intelligence suitable for the workplace

J

Job: A regular activity performed in exchange for payment, especially as one's trade, occupation, or profession

L

Large-cap fund: Funds comprised of large, well-established companies

Lease: A long-term rental agreement, and a form of secured long-term debt

Legacy: Anything handed down from the past; something that someone has achieved that continues to exist after they are gone

Level term: This means you pay the same amount for the entire term of the policy

Liability: The state or quality of being obligated according to law or equity

Liability insurance: Policy that protects an individual in the event of a lawsuit due to injury on one's personal property or as the result of an automobile accident

Life insurance: Type of insurance designed to replace income lost due to death; traditionally two types: term and cash value

Liquidity: Quality of an asset that permits it to be converted quickly into cash without loss of value; availability of money

Loan: Temporary borrowing of a sum of money

Load fund: Mutual fund that sells shares with a sales charge of typically 2-6% of the net amount sold; some no-load funds also levy distribution fees permitted by Article 12b-1 of the Investment Company Act. These are typically 0.25%; a true no- load fund has no sales charge.

Loan term: Time frame that a loan agreement is in force, and before or at the end of which the loan should either be repaid or renegotiated for another term

Loan to value (LTV): Value of a property versus the amount borrowed against it; example: a 70/30 LTV means that the property owner owes 70% of the item's worth and owns 30% of the item's worth

Long-term care insurance: Policy that covers the cost of nursing home or in-home care; recommended for everyone over age 60

Long-term coverage: Coverage for an extended period of time

Long-term disability: Disability insurance designed to replace lost income for a period of five years or greater

Loss: The negative difference between total revenue from a business or investment minus total expense

Low-load fund: Mutual fund that charges a sales commission equal to 3% or less of the amount invested

M

Management fee: The fee paid by a mutual fund to its investment advisor

Marketing: The process of communicating the value of a product or service to customers

Market risk: The possibility that an investment will fall in value due to a general decline in financial markets

Markup: The difference between the wholesale price and retail price

Maximum pay: The amount an insurance company will pay before you are dropped from coverage. With health insurance keep at least a one million dollar maximum pay

Medicare: Federal government program that pays for certain health care expenses for citizens 65 or older; managed by the Social Security Administration

Mid-cap fund: Mutual fund containing a group of medium-sized companies that are growing

Money: Currency and coin that are guaranteed as legal tender by the government

Money market fund: Mutual fund that seeks to maintain a stable share price and to earn current income by investing in interest-bearing instruments with short-term (usually 90 days or less) maturities

Money order: A financial instrument backed by a deposit at a certain firm, such as a bank, that can be easily converted to cash

Mortgage: Loan secured by the collateral of some specified real estate property, which obligates the borrower to make a predetermined series of payments

Mortgage life insurance: Insurance policy that pays off the remaining balance of the insured person's mortgage at death

Mutual fund: Pool of money managed by an investment company and invested in multiple companies, bonds, etc.; offers investors a variety of goals depending on the fund and its investment charter; often used to generate income on a regular basis or to preserve an investor's money; sometimes used to invest in companies that are growing at a rapid pace

Myth: Information that has been passed on but is not true

N

Need: Economic goods and services that are basic for living such as food, clothing, and shelter

Negotiate: To bargain for a lower price

Nerd: A person who is picky about budgeting and details

Nest egg: Sum of money earmarked for ongoing living expenses at retirement or when employment income otherwise stops

Net asset value (NAV): The market value of a mutual fund's total assets, less its liabilities, divided by the number of outstanding shares

Nonprofits: Organizations that use money raised to achieve their goals rather than distributing them as profit

No-load mutual fund: Open-ended investment company whose shares are sold without a sales charge; might include other distribution charges, such as Article 12b-1 fees, but a true no-load fund has neither a sales charge nor a distribution fee

Objective: A goal or plan

Occupational disability: Type of insurance that provides an income in case the insured becomes unable to perform the job he/she was educated or trained to do

Opportunity cost: Refers to the financial opportunity that is given up because you choose to do something else with your money

Out-of-pocket expense: Specific amount of money that you pay when insurance only covers a portion of costs

Owner financing: Type of home loan in which the existing owner acts as the mortgage holder; payments are made to the owner rather than to a mortgage company or bank

Overdraft: Occurs when money is withdrawn from a bank account and the available balance goes below zero

P

Paradigm: Your belief system; the way you see or perceive things

Passive income: Money earned on a regular basis with little or no effort required to maintain it. Some things that produce passive income are real estate, intellectual property like books or internet content, or a business in which the owner is not actively involved.

Pawn shop: Retail establishment selling items that have been traded as security for a cash loan

Payroll deduction: Amount subtracted from a paycheck, either by government requirement (mandatory taxes, Social Security, etc.) or at the employee's request (health insurance, retirement plan, etc.)

Permanent disability: Disabilities that are ongoing and are not expected to end

Personal branding: The process by which we "market" ourselves to others; involves highlighting personal strengths, interests and unique qualities and identifying goals

Personal finance: The decisions which an individual or a family unit is required to make to obtain, budget, save, and spend money over time

Philanthropy: Means "love of humanity"; identifying and exercising one's values in giving and volunteering

Policy: Describes the type of coverage in an insurance agreement

Portfolio: A list of your investments

Portfolio income: Income generated by selling an investment at a higher price than you paid for it

Portfolio transaction costs: The costs associated with buying and selling securities, including commissions on trades, dealer mark-ups on bonds, bid-asking spreads, and any other miscellaneous expenses. These costs are not included in the expense ratio.

Pre-authorized checking (PAC): System of automatic payment processing by which bills, deposits, and payments are handled electronically and at regular intervals or on a predetermined schedule

Pre-paid tuition: Paying for college ahead of time by accumulating units of tuition

Pre-tax retirement plan: A type of retirement plan where you put money in before taxes have been taken out, but must pay taxes on the money at the time of withdrawal

Premium: Amount you pay monthly, quarterly, semi-annually or annually to purchase different types of Insurance

Principal: Original amount of money invested, excluding any interest or dividends; also called the face value of a loan

Priority: Level of high importance or great urgency

Private mortgage insurance (PMI): Policy paid by the mortgage borrower that protects the lender against loss resulting from default on a mortgage loan

Profit: The positive difference between total revenue from a business or investment minus total expense

Property taxes: Taxes paid by anyone who owns property such as land, a home or commercial real estate

Pro rata: Debt repayment plan by which the borrower repays each lender a fair percentage of the total debt owed when one cannot make the minimum payments on one's debt

Prospectus: Official document that contains information required by the Securities and Exchange Commission to describe an investment

R

Rate of return: Return on an investment expressed as a percentage of its cost; also called yield

Realtor: An intermediary who receives a commission for arranging and facilitating the sale of a property for a buyer or a seller; also referred to as a Real Estate Broker or an Agent

Reconcile: To match your bank statement with your checkbook

Redemption fee: Fee charged by some mutual funds for selling (redeeming) shares

Refunding: Sending in proofs of purchase to receive cash back or free gifts

Reinvestment: Use of investment income or dividends to buy additional shares

Rent: Periodic fee for the use of property

Rental real estate: Buying real estate to rent out as an investment

Renter's insurance: Type of insurance that provides coverage for accidents, damages and losses in a rental (apartment or house) or dormitory. Renter's insurance provides coverage for personal belongings and liability that may occur from an accident in the insured home

Replacement cost: Insurance that pays the actual cost of replacing your home and its contents after a catastrophic event

Repo lot: A place where items that have been repossessed are offered for sale

Restoration services: Part of identity theft insurance that assigns a counselor to clean up the mess made when your identity was stolen

Résumé: A brief account of one's professional or work experience and qualifications, often submitted with an employment application

Retailer: One who buys a product to re-sell

Reverse mortgage: Used to release the home equity in a property. The home owner either makes no payments and the interest is added to the lien of the property, or receives monthly payments thereby increasing the debt each month.

Risk: Degree of uncertainty of return on an asset; in business, the likelihood of loss or reduced profit

Risk-return ratio: Relationship of substantial reward compared to the amount of risk taken

Rollover: Movement of funds from a tax-deferred retirement plan from one qualified plan or custodian to another; incurs no immediate tax liabilities or penalties, but requires IRS reporting

Roth IRA: Retirement account funded with after-tax dollars that subsequently grows tax free

Roth 401(k): Employer-sponsored retirement savings account that is funded with after-tax dollars and subsequently grows tax free

Rule of 72: A quick way to calculate the length of time it will take to double a sum of money. Divide 72 by the expected interest rate to determine the number of years (72 divided by 8% = 9 years).

Rule of 78: Pre-payment penalty in a financing contract; the portion of a 90-days-same-as-cash agreement that states that the entire loan amount plus the interest accumulated over the first 90 days becomes due immediately

S

Salary: Payment for work, usually calculated in periods of a week or longer. Salary is usually tied to the completion of specific duties over a minimum, but not maximum, number of hours. (See wage.)

Sales tax: Tax on goods and services that goes to your state or local government

Saving: The process of setting aside money until a future date instead of spending it today. The goal is to provide for emergencies, short term goals, and investments.

Savings account: Accounts at financial institutions that allow regular deposits and withdrawals. The minimum required deposit, fees charged, and interest rate paid varies among providers.

Savings bond: Certificate representing a debt; example: U.S. savings bond is a loan to the government in which the government agrees to repay to the bondholder the amount borrowed, with interest; government bonds are issued in face value denominations from $50 to $10,000, with local and state tax-free interest and semi-annually adjusted interest rates.

Savings & loan associations (S&Ls): Financial institutions that provide loans and interest bearing accounts which are federally insured

Scholarship: A form of financial aid that does not need to be repaid; usually awarded on the basis of academic, athletic or other achievements

Sector fund: A mutual fund that invests its shareholders' money in a relatively narrow market sector, e.g. technology, energy, the internet, or banking

Security: The state of being free from danger or threat

Self-esteem: A confidence and satisfaction in yourself

Self-insured: Condition of wealth at which time one no longer needs an outside insurance policy to cover a loss

Share: Piece of ownership in a company, mutual fund or other investment

Short-term disability: Minimal period of incapacitation; often used to describe an insurance policy that insures one's income for the immediate future following an incapacitating event

Short-term policy: Insurance policy that only covers a minimal period of time

Significant purchase: An amount of money you spend, usually $300, that causes some pain to part with

Simple interest: Interest credited daily, monthly, quarterly, semi-annually, or annually on principal only, not previously credited interest

Simple IRA: Salary deduction plan for retirement benefits provided by some small companies with fewer than 100 employees

Simplified employee pension plan (SEPP): Pension plan in which both the employee and the employer contribute to an individual retirement account; also available to the self-employed

Sinking fund: Saving money over time for a large purchase

Small-cap fund: Mutual fund that invests in companies whose market value is less than $1 billion; largely consists of smaller, more volatile companies; also called aggressive growth stock mutual fund

Social Security: A federal insurance program funded by taxpayer dollars that provides benefits to people who are retired, unemployed or disabled

Speculative: Purchasing risky investments that present the possibility of large profits, but also pose a higher-than-average possibility of loss

Stock markets:

» **National Association of Securities Dealers Automated Quotation System (NASDAQ):** The electronic stock exchange run by the National Association of Securities Dealers for over the counter trading. Established in 1971, it is America's fastest growing stock market and a leader in trading foreign securities and technology shares. The NASDAQ uses market makers who trade for their own account and profit on the spread between bid and ask prices. Although once the province of smaller companies, NASDAQ today is where many leading companies are traded.

» **New York Stock Exchange (NYSE):** The NYSE traces its origins back more that 200 years to the signing of the Buttonwood Agreement by 24 New York City stockbrokers and merchants in 1792. The NYSE utilizes a trading floor for traditional exchanges where buyers and sellers meet directly–that is, brokers representing investors on each side of the transaction come together on a price.

Stocks: Securities that represent part ownership or equity in a corporation

Stop-loss: Total out-of-pocket expense for health insurance; once reached, insurance will pay 100 percent

T

Take-home pay: The amount of money one has available after taxes have been taken out of their pay; total wage, salary, commissions, and/or bonuses minus payroll deductions

Tax: A government fee on business and individual income, activities, products, or services

Tax credit: An amount that a taxpayer who meets certain criteria can subtract from tax owed

Tax deduction: Expense that a taxpayer is allowed to deduct from taxable income; examples include money paid as home mortgage interest and charitable donations

Tax deductible: The effect of a tax deduction, such as charitable contributions and mortgage interest

Tax-deferred income: Dividends, interest, and unrealized capital gains on investments in a qualified account, such as a retirement plan, in which income is not subject to taxation until a withdrawal is made

Tax exempt: Investments whose earnings are free from tax liability

Tax exemptions: Amount that a taxpayer who meets certain criteria can subtract from a taxable income; see tax credit and tax deduction

Tax-favored dollars: Money that is invested, either tax deferred or tax free, within a retirement plan

Taxable income: Income subject to tax; total income adjusted for deductions, exemptions and credits

Teamwork: Cooperative and coordinated effort on the part of a group of persons acting together in the interest of a common goal

Term insurance: Life insurance coverage for a specified period of time

Time poverty: A situation in which a person is lacking time, which leads to stress

Timeshare: A form of vacation property ownership where a company sells a small segment of time (usually a week) to a customer. The use and costs of running the property are shared among all of the customers, now owners, who bought into the timeshare.

Time value of money: Money at the present time is worth more than the same amount in the future

Title insurance: Coverage that protects a policyholder from future challenges to the title of a property that may result in loss of the property

Total return: The change in percentage over a particular period in the value of an investment; including any income from the investment and any change in its market value

Track record: The past history of something; with investments, look at the five or ten year record

Turnover rate: A measure of a mutual fund's trading activity. Turnover is calculated by taking the lesser of the fund's total purchases or total sales of securities (not counting securities with maturities under one year) and dividing by the average monthly assets. A turnover rate of 50% means that during a year, a fund has sold and replaced securities with a value equal to 50% of the fund's average net assets.

U

Umbrella liability insurance: High-limit insurance policy that acts as a protective covering over your home and car insurance against liability caused by an accident

Underwriter: A firm that buys an issue of securities from a company and resells it to investors; in general, a party that guarantees the proceeds to the firm from a security sale, thereby in effect taking ownership of the securities

Unearned income: Money received for which no exchange was made, such as a gift

Uniform Gifts to Minors Act (UGMA): Legislation that provides a tax-effective manner of transferring property to minors without the complications of trusts or guardianship restrictions

Uniform Transfers to Minors Act (UTMA): Law similar to the Uniform Gifts to Minors Act (UGMA) that extends the definition of gifts to include real estate, paintings, royalties, and patents

Universal life: Type of life insurance policy, similar to cash value, but with better projected returns

Unrealized capital gain/loss: An increase/decrease in the value of a stock or security (mutual fund) that is not "realized" because the security has not yet been sold for a gain or a loss

V

Veterans Administration (VA) loan: Type of mortgage loan designed to benefit veterans that allows for a true zero-down mortgage; generally more expensive than a conventional mortgage

Value fund: Mutual fund that emphasizes stocks of companies whose growth prospects are generally regarded as sub-par by the market, resulting in stocks typically priced below average based on such factors as revenue, earnings, book value, and dividends

Value system: A person's priorities, beliefs and standards that affect how he or she views the world

Variable annuity: Annuity that has a varying rate of return based on the mutual funds in which one has invested; also see annuity

Variable life: Type of life insurance that is similar to cash value, but buys into mutual funds to project better returns

Viatical: Contractual arrangement in which a business buys life insurance policies from terminally ill patients for a percentage of the face value

Vocation: What you do for a living that is your "calling"

Volatility: Fluctuations in market value of a mutual fund or other security; the greater a fund's volatility, the wider the fluctuations between high and low prices

W

W-4: A federal tax form filled out by an employee to indicate the amount that should be withheld from his/her paycheck for taxes

Wage: Payment for work, usually calculated in periods of an hour rather than longer (see salary)

Walk-away power: The ability to walk away from a purchase when negotiating

Wants: Desires for economic goods or services not necessary in order to survive

Wealth: Accumulating assets such as money and possessions, often as a result of saving or investing

Will: A legally enforceable declaration of how a person wishes his or her property to be distributed after death

Withholding: A portion of employee's wages or salary deducted for taxes

Whole life insurance: Type of insurance that contains a low-yield savings plan within the insurance policy; more expensive than term life insurance

Work ethic: How motivated, loyal and honest you are in your work

Work study: A program that allows students to work part time while continuing their studies

Y

Yield: The annualized rate at which an investment earns income, expressed as a percentage of the investment's current price

Z

Zero-based budget: A cash flow plan that assigns an expense to every dollar of your income, wherein the total income minus the total expenses equals zero

Student Achievement Certificate

Now that you've learned the key principles taught in Foundations in Personal Finance, *you can earn a personalized Certificate of Achievement recognizing your accomplishment!*

To Get the Certificate

1 Go to **foundationsU.com/high-school** and click on "Certification."

2 Complete a randomized twenty-question quiz that will test your knowledge of the principles discussed in the *Foundations in Personal Finance* curriculum. Don't overthink this! All of the questions will be based on the information you learned.

3 After you pass the quiz with a score of 80% or higher, you'll get a personalized Certificate of Achievement ready for you to download and print so you can save it or share it with your parents or teacher.

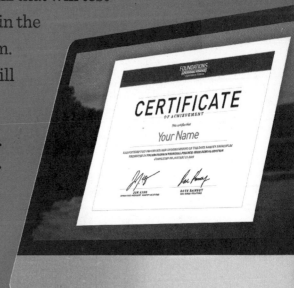